Buckmxn Journal presents

This Is Portland

Portland, OR
buckmanjournal.com
Buckman Publishing, LLC

Buckmxn Journal Crew

Jerry Sampson
Scout

Emmi Greer
Managing Editor

Ellen Robinette
Art Director

Hannah Johnson
Designer

Rich Perin
Barback

What's Inside

1 Introduction

2 "Driving"
Comic by Erin Nations

3 The Mayor
Story by Rich Perin

6 Profile: Chris Nesseth

9 Silver Fox
Story by J.T. Townley | Paintings by Violet Aveline

18 Cute Meat Does Portland
Recipes & photos by Kourtney Paranteau

27 "Try Harder"
Collage by Yuyang Zhang

28 Bad Memory
Essay by Scott Korb | Photography by Sylvie Huhn

34 "Stuffed Rabbit"
Comic by Liz Yerby

35 Oregon Grown
Foreword & interviews by Lauren Yoshiko |
Photos by Christine Dong

45 The Day I Quit Instacart
Flash Fiction by Tracey Nguyen

47 A Bear, A Possum, and Two Girls
Walk Into A Strip Club
Story by Michelle Ruiz Keil | Illustrations by
Tomás Oliveras

57 "Formula No. 1" & "Just A Sip"
Mixed media art by Morgan Rosskopf

59 A Quiet Song
Story by Alex Grejuc | Paintings by Josh Gates

67 A Progressive Tarot Reading
for the City of Portland
Foreword & curation by Coleman Stevenson |
Readings by Given Q. Davis, Stephanie Adams-
Santos, Michelle Ruiz Keil & Erik L. Arneson | Card
illustration by Michael Armenia

79 Hape Waiu
Poem, photo & printmaking by Jordan DeLawder

81 "Full Moon Heart"
Mixed media art by Morgan Rosskopf

83 Kill Them with Kindness
Story by Stacy Brewster | Illustrations by Pace Taylor

93 Poetry by Vandoren Wheeler
2022 Recipient of the Buckman Journal Poetry Prize

103 Photos by Chris Nesseth

105 Corbin's Disposable Camera Snapshots
Flash Non-fiction & photos by Corbin Corbin

111 Racism: The Movie
Story by Chris Stuck

117 The Sequence of Summer Dreams
Story by Vivian McInerny | Collage by Lara Rouse

121 "Small Pleasures"
Comic by Erin Nations

123 Exit Interview: Oliver Kautter

131 The People of Pithom
Story by J.G.P. MacAdam | Photos by
Yuyang Zhang

136 Death of an Applicant
Poetry by Jaye Nasir | Paintings by
Janice Minjin Yang

141 The Rabbit in the Moon
Story by Susan DeFreitas | Paintings by
Erica Peebus

149 Photo by Chris Nesseth

Front & back cover photos by Chris Nesseth

This is Portland

Word-of-mouth is *the* method of transmission in Portland. It's a long-standing practice, dating back to speakeasies and Shanghai Tunnels. It goes something like this:

Someone, maybe a friendly stranger at a bar or cafe, will tell you about a show on a particular night at an old warehouse or abandoned lot or under a freeway overpass. You go to the show, and it's a band or burlesque or dance troupe or something multi-art and genre breaking. You chat with other people there, learn of other happenings, and have a fun and unexpected night.

That's Portland.

It's a city where artists, writers, and musicians have flocked since the 1990s. It's where they grow, hopefully to expand their talent and skills, with the understanding that not all attempts will work. Portland makes room for mistakes. The attempt is what matters. And when attempts do work, the audience is richly rewarded.

When someone proclaims that Portland lacks diversity, the reality refutes. Such proclaimers need reminder of Portland's word-of-mouth credentials. *Just because you don't know of something happening doesn't mean it isn't happening.* The diversity is out there plenty, whether cultural or style. The grapevine grows long, beyond the backyard.

THIS IS PORTLAND is a result of running along *some* of the grapevines.

A travel guide tells you where to go and what to eat. *THIS IS PORTLAND* goes further. By presenting the city's acclaimed artists and writers, as well as its unique cultural innovators, this book conveys the soul and spirit of Portland like no other.

3

The Mayor

Story: RICH PERIN (he/him)

It was around midnight, and I was too restless for sleep. I had spent an hour in bed, flipping from side to side, eyes closed but sharply awake, until I realized that fighting for sleep fattened the frustration. Since my body called for movement, it seemed, why was I against it? So, I arose, slipped on jeans, and went for a walk around the Buckman neighborhood, no destination or route in mind, a casual stroll to admire the gentle sway of leafy trees and architecture of old houses. It was about twenty minutes into this walkabout that I found myself across the street from one of the local dives. I took this as another sign and went inside for a nightcap.

There was noise of someone playing pinball in the side room, but the bar was empty, and Dezarae the bartender looked like she was sleeping with her eyes open. As I approached, she came to, blinking, then stretched her arms above her head as she yawned. "Gawd, Rich, I'm so glad to have some company. It's slow death in here." She grabbed the bottle of Maker's Mark and poured a long shot on rocks in a tumbler.

"It's a Tuesday," I said. "Respectable people are home, falling asleep in front of Netflix, if they aren't sleeping already."

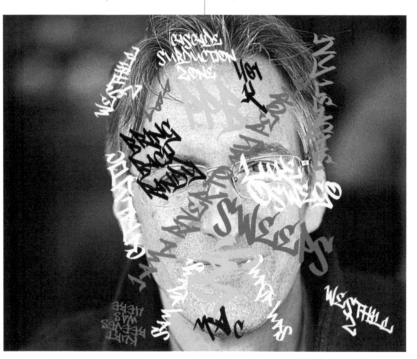

"A few poked their heads in, but they sensed the bad vibes coming from the back." Dezarae nodded over her left shoulder.

I didn't notice the figure in the back of the bar, which surprised me because I take pride in reading a room when I enter it. The figure was wearing a black hoodie, seated by the rear wall where light was the least. The silhouette wasn't ominous, it didn't have a confident gait and, aside from the low light, another reason I didn't notice was the slight and waifish size of the stranger. Despite this, Dezarae was right. There was a creepy vibe, like a gargoyle.

"Huh. Doesn't look old enough to drink," I said.

"It's the Mayor," said Dezarae.

"What?"

"That's the Mayor sitting back there."

"That's what I thought you said. That can't be the Mayor. It looks like a moody teenager."

"When he walked in, I thought it was a kid, too, his hoodie hiding his head and all. But then he pulled out his ID, and I got a good look at his face. Definitely not a kid. Middle-aged. Mayor's face. Mayor's name. West Hills address."

"Are you for real?"

"Yes. When he came in, it looked like he had been crying," said Dezarae. "I was going to suggest he should drink elsewhere but then I thought better of it. He's the Mayor, I can't refuse him no matter how unlikeable he is."

"Sure, back in the day it was stupid to cross the mayor. Not so much these days, but why ignore history and dare its return. The mayor can still fuck you over. What's he drinking? It looks like orange juice."

"He ordered a Harvey Wallbanger,"

"You're kidding."

"Really. He came in and asked for a Harvey Wallbanger. I laughed, but he was serious."

"Yeah, yeah," I spoke, recalling the cocktail. "Orange juice, vodka and Galliano, the Italian liqueur that comes in a real tall skinny bottle. I haven't seen it in years."

"Yeah, I said something similar, about how my grandparents may have a bottle of Galliano, but this place doesn't. Anyways, I talked him into a screwdriver, and then it takes most of an hour for him to drink it. When he came back for his second it looked like he cried some more."

"You know, it's admirable when elected officials mingle with the community they represent," I said. "Real mingling. Man of the people stuff. But our mayor isn't like that. Silver spoons, West Hills set, milquetoast, pearly white clean. I'm surprised he dared to set foot in a grimy place like this."

Dezarae furrowed her eyes.

"No offense, Dez, you know I like this bar. I prefer low light and grit, the sweat and cough in the walls. Our mayor, he wines and dines in swank West Side bistros with white starched servers and twenty-dollar drinks."

"Maybe we all got it wrong," said Dezarae. "Maybe he is

on our side."

"Yeah," I said smiling. "Right. On our side." I stood up and walked to the back table.

It was the Mayor. On closer look and once my eyes accustomed to the low light, there was no doubt, although his face was drained and pale. He was quietly sobbing, not even trying to hide it, eyes downward to the table, looking through it.

"Hey, buddy, is everything alright?" I asked.

It took a little while for him to build a whimpered response. "I, I, I don't... know."

"Life's not treating you kind, eh?" I took a seat next to him. "Be mindful what you're drinking. Alcohol tends to make life heavier, which is appropriate in some circumstances."

"Orange juice upsets my stomach. I don't know why I am drinking it. I should have ordered a wine spritzer."

"Jesus. That's just sad. What's bugging you?"

"No one likes me," he declared in a raised, emotionally charged pitch. "Nothing I do makes anyone happy!" Then the tears really fell freely, soaking his face.

"Well, yeah, that's a shame, real sad," I spoke soothingly, delivering tones of reassurance and empathy. "These are extremely troubling times, things got weird during the pandemic. Some rise to the challenge. Most don't and drown."

"Yes, drowning, that's how I feel! Hopelessly drowning!"

"Come now, that's no way to speak," I patted him on his shoulder. "After all, a man of your position should never feel like that. You represent the city. This is what you signed up for."

The Mayor lifted his head and looked at me closely for the first time. His eyes were wild and red and flooded. "Look around!" he yelled. "Homeless camps everywhere. The police have my nuts in a vice. Drag racers take over Fremont bridge on Sunday nights and spin donuts. And someone stole my ex-wife's catalytic convertor, which she blames on me, of course."

"Well, yes, like I said, things got weird, this is what happens during a pandemic. Other things have happened too, good things. It's just you weren't the reason for them either."

"What? It's not my fault!"

I let him own the silence, letting his plead of innocence linger alone in the air. Then I suggested as a conciliary, "Still, things could have been better."

The Mayor shook his head. "See? You don't like me, too! Why are you talking to me?"

"I'm not going to embellish your record any more than I have. You won't get bullshit from me, Mister Mayor. I am sincere. I don't think mine's an unfair critique. I bet most people usually scream bloody murder when they see you in public."

This logic settled him. "Yes, that's true," he said, lowering his voice. "You have been sincere. And people usually do yell at me."

"But I'm not yelling at you, Mister Mayor, am I?"

He nodded. "You know, I want to help people. When I graduated from Harvard, I knew that public service was my calling. I think it's what JFK felt." He then began to ramble on about his achievements; the three years at Cambridge and summer sojourns in Santorini; his triumphant reorganization of his family's wood harvesting empire; how he became a mountaineer and climbed the world's tallest peaks, and that sometime next year he and a few chums from the Multnomah Athletics Club were going to summit Mount Rainier. He mindlessly finished his screwdriver while recounting. It made him feel good and proud, verbalizing a few of the things he accomplished, to hear them aloud and have someone listening, well, appearing to listen.

I stopped him when he started talking about the environmentally friendly credentials of his stock portfolio. "Come on, this isn't your type of place," I said. "Let's get out of here and get you another drink."

"Where are we going?"

"Down the street."

I wished a goodnight to Dez, and she responded in kind but only to me. As the Mayor and I exited the bar a small group of people entered behind us.

We walked by another bar. "I thought we were going to another bar," said the Mayor.

"You don't need more alcohol. We're going to Plaid Panties, get you a Gatorade."

The Mayor giggled. "Plaid Panties. Ha! I like that."

"Man, it's like you are not from here. Listen, you need to sober. We'll go into the Plaid, get you a Gatorade, and maybe a box of hot pockets."

"Hot pockets give me heartburn."

"Whatever. Get a chocolate muffin, anything, you need something in your gut."

The aisles of Plaid Pantry convenience stores are lit by shameless lights, the cheapest of all fluorescent, emitting a spectrum so off scale that it probably carries x-rays. Its cruelness dives deep, reveals every microfracture on the skin, radiating the blemishes and hair follicles. The photons are not collected by eyes, rather they attack with sabers. But I admire this ugly light, its uniqueness, its brazenness, how it's not the same during the day, its full ferocity only coming out during the midnight hours.

The Mayor hated it. As soon as he opened the door he recoiled, but I pushed him inside. "Why are you doing this to me?" he whimpered.

"You need to sober. Just because alcohol is legal doesn't mean everyone can handle it. Alcohol teaches self-capacity. You've found yours. Now is the time for you to get a soda."

The Mayor used a hand to shelter his face and shuffled into a Cheetos display. "It hurts my eyes in here. And my ears," he said. The ring of the fluorescent lights challenged the volume of the radio behind the register.

"Yeah, soak it up," I said. "It makes you stronger."

The Mayor waddled towards the iced-teas, eyes wincing, arms outstretched in front to ensure he wouldn't walk into anything else. He was mesmerized in the snack aisle, debating what to choose, so he examined every offering and finally picked an obscure bag of mini pretzels stuffed with processed cheese. The bearded Plaid Pantry worker didn't say a word as he rang up the Mayor. It was only after payment was approved and the Mayor said thanks as he walked out of the store that the worker spoke up and replied with a fuck you. The Mayor heard it but didn't react.

We walked up Belmont towards Colonel Summers park. I talked about how a streetcar line used to run all the way to the canneries and warehouses down by the riverfront, and how it was the epicenter of the labor protests in the early 1900s. The Mayor didn't add anything to the conversation, and only burped and mumbled about his "sour belly."

At Colonel Summers park, the Mayor found the playground and sat on a swing. He put no effort into swinging, no attempt to regain a sense of childhood joy, it was only a place for him to sit, let his feet drag while he consumed his mini pretzels and canned tea. "I'm usually at home asleep at this hour," he said. "But I couldn't sleep, I just had a compulsion to walk, and I walked all the way across the river to here."

"Cool," I said. "What did you see?"

"I don't really remember. I was wracked with worry, thinking things over."

"That's a shame, to walk without looking. It's a nice city to experience on foot, so many things you miss in a car driving from point a to b."

"I guess so," said the Mayor, his mouth full of mush.

"I mean, look around now. That's a redwood over there. Its bark is like nature's braille. Give it a read. And look at how moon-white that cloud is."

The Mayor lifted his head and surveyed the surroundings. "Yeah, it is kind of nice and peaceful," he said, and he stopped munching his pretzels, to watch and appreciate.

The moment of accord changed when a tagger in a hoodie appeared across the street from the park, freestyling tags on mailboxes, sidewalks, street signs, whatever took his fancy. "Look at that asshole," I said to the Mayor. "Sometimes I want to set aside my pacifism and slap people like that. Not closed-fisted. A healthy slap across the face."

"Settle down," hushed the Mayor. "Maybe that kid down there just needs someone to appreciate him, to guide him. He might be the next Picasso."

"What kind of horseshit is that?" I responded. "That's an insult to Picasso, damn, to every respectable artist."

"Who's to say what is good and bad?"

"Obviously not you."

"And you are?"

"Sure, yes, me. And anyone who has a brain. There is clearly a difference between Picasso and a tagger."

"But that tagger is just beginning," objected the Mayor. "Maybe he'll improve. I wouldn't be surprised if the teenage Picasso was a tagger."

"Yeah, you're delusional," I said. "Besides, that's no teenager down there. That's some dude in his thirties, lives with his mom, sells stuff on eBay."

The Mayor took a hard look. "His hoodie hides his face, I can't make it out, but that shape is not of a grown man."

"This is the first time you've seen a tagger at work, eh?"

"Well, I have addressed a few street mural openings."

"That's a dumb comparison."

"I just think that's a kid down there," said the Mayor, "and some encouragement, some guidance and support, might go a long way."

"You believe what you will. But consider the history of your perceptions."

The Mayor snarled, "What does that mean? Darn it, I know how to settle this," and he stood from the swing and marched to the corner at the end of the block, where the tagger was Picassoing over a stop sign.

I couldn't exactly make out what the Mayor was saying, but it wasn't delivered with compassion and empathy. Yelling between the two erupted, disengagement and then more engagement, and in the dark and distance I lost which hoodie was who. They were silhouettes, shouting at each other, breaking the peace in what was a dark and gentle night.

There was no satisfaction in staying so I left, walking several blocks until I could no longer hear the argument from Colonel Summers park. The trees were thriving, their canopy thick, and the streetlights failed to penetrate, leaving stretches of sidewalk so dark that it felt like walking in outer space. I found myself outside the old Victorian that has three giant elms in front, looking upwards trying to make out their heights, when I felt something sniffing at my feet. It was a raccoon pup, young and naïve that its inquisitiveness overrode its primal sense of survival. It oozed cuteness, only a few inches longer than my boot. I cooed a "Hello, fella." Then from the elms scampered two more pups, merrily chirping, joining their sibling's investigation. I didn't hang around for long, their mother was surely nearby, and she would be ready to throw it down at the sight of her pups so close to an apex predator. There are good reasons why most animals avoid humans. We are packed with ignorance and are reckless with it, our capacity to deliver harm limitless. I walked away, before a bond could form, but the pups followed. I shooed and hissed which only made them come closer and chirp with more enthusiasm, as if they found me hilarious. I broke into a sprint, and I lost them around a corner.

🅑

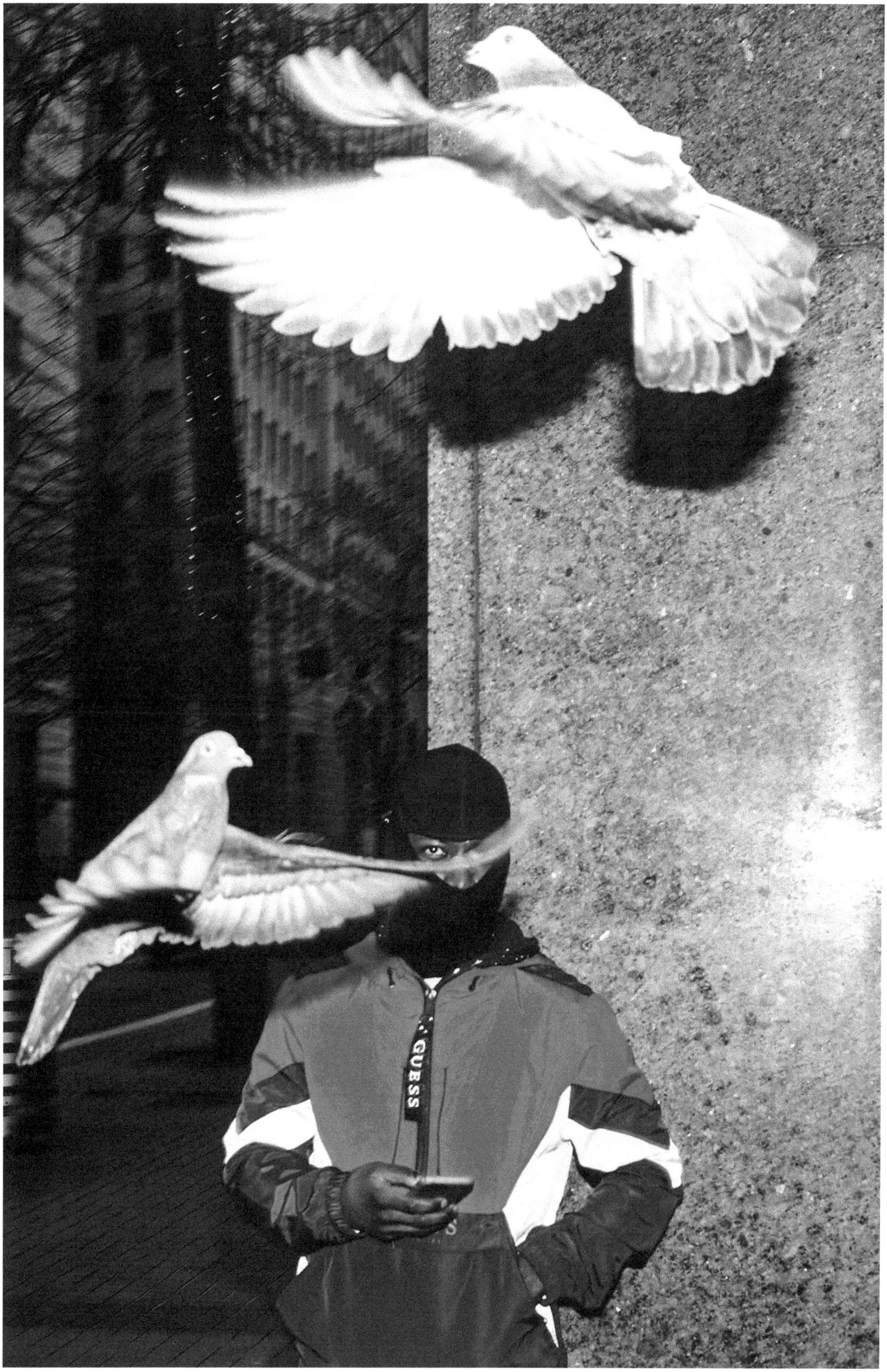

Photo by Chris Nesseth

PROFILE

Chris Nesseth
(he/him)

Art paparazzo. That's Chris Nesseth. Recognizing the everyday as the celebrity. Capturing moments of great candor.

Timing is everything in photography. Some may suggest light, but even light comes down to time. The right spot at the right time. A split second before or after changes the result, misses the moment.

Timing can be learned, more or less, but there's a difference between being born with perfect timing and learning it.

Chris Nesseth is from Wyoming. An avid hiker, he moved to the Pacific Northwest to exploit its super abundance of natural geography and fauna. He got a job in Portland. Car salesman. Life was good.

Then he got a DUI. Lost his car. Couldn't get out of town to the trailheads. The desire for movement didn't cease so he started walking around the city. "Might as well bring a camera with me," he reasoned. Outside of a smartphone, Chris Nesseth didn't know much about photography.

This is where his perfect timing became known.

He honed composition skills. Grew an appreciation for color. He discovered a talent for photography. More than a talent.

He quit his job as a car salesman.

Freelance photographer is his trade.

He hasn't hiked in the wilderness since his DUI. Doesn't feel the same need to be in nature as he used to. His eyes are enamored by downtown. ⓑ

Chris Nesseth is a street photographer and a photojournalist whose work is often found in *Willamette Week*.
@chrisnesseth

Photo by Chris Nesseth

Silver Fox

Story: J.T. TOWNLEY (he/him)

J.T. Townley's writing has appeared in *Harvard Review, The Kenyon Review, The Threepenny Review*, and dozens of other magazines and journals. J.T holds an MFA in Creative Writing from the University of British Columbia, and an MPhil in English from the University of Oxford.
www.jttownley.com

Paintings: VIOLET AVELINE (she/her)

To paraphrase Joshua Hughes, the art of Violet Aveline takes on heaviness, often brutally, while injecting levity with gallows humor.

I was so fixated on her hair, dull gray and shaped like a Halloween wig, I almost missed her snickering as she scanned the Manly Man package. The tag on her smock read Verity. She shook her head as she rang up my Life Preservers, ibuprofen, and *Stumptown Telegram*, then stuffed it all into a bag. The door chime rang.

"Kind of judgy, aren't you?" I said.

She gave me a wary glance, jaw working a wad of gum, then punched keys on her register. Her Li Stick-On Nails matched her gray hair. She couldn't have been older than twenty-five. "No judgment," she said.

"What do you think your manager would say?"

Her face turned to stone. "$37.93," she announced.

I fished my wallet out and plugged my card into the reader.

As Verity tore off my receipt and slipped it into the bag, she forced a smile. I wanted to ask how old she was and didn't she know her hair would go gray on its own? But when I opened my mouth to speak, nothing came out.

"Be careful with it," she said.

I groped for the box, scanning the safety warnings. "Careful?"

The door chimed again. A pair of twenty-somethings in skinny jeans sauntered in. I studied their gray bobs as they disappeared down the hair-care aisle. Verity smacked her gum.

"Is it still raining outside?" she asked.

"Probably, why?"

Verity examined her nail polish, then fiddled with her middle finger where the fake nail had come loose. "Simple," she said. "That stuff runs."

As I pedaled through downtown, then over the Murphy bridge, I goggled at all the gray hair. It had nothing to do with age. Schoolgirls in St. Margaret's Academy hoodies, cross-country runners from a local college, and professionals in pantsuits were all sporting various hues of gray. Even a couple of guys in their twenties with neck tattoos were rocking the granny hair. I slowed my pace, staring. It didn't make any sense. Everyone was heading that direction already, so what was the rush?

I left the river behind and rode the last mile home. The evening smelled green and wet. When I pushed into my empty apartment, I sank into the couch in the dim light, struggling to figure out why I was so worked up. People wore all sorts of wild hair colors: blue and pink, neon green, multicolor rainbow. Gray was just another color, right? Wrong. I'd read an article about it in *Healthy Man*: in physiological terms, gray was what happened when hair follicles stopped producing pigment. So it wasn't a color. It was a condition.

The next day, Katie was on my case soon as I came through the door, scowling in a miasma of soy sauce, vinegar, and chives. She managed Ensō, though I'd been there so long, I knew how the place ran better than anyone. By now, we were friends, but that didn't keep her from being a stickler. It was what the owner paid her for.

"What do you call that look?" she said as I clocked in. "Drowned rat chic?"

"Morning, Boss."

"You're so late, it's almost afternoon."

I ran a hand through my hair, tucked my shirt in, and tied on my apron. The prep cooks argued in Spanish about soccer.

"Seriously, Jimmy. You look terrible."

"Thanks," I said, studying the specials board and scribbling in my notebook.

"What'd you get into last night?"

I slipped my pen and notebook back into my apron, then glanced up. I blinked and rubbed my eyes. When I focused again, I stood there, gawking at her. She'd been a brunette, but now her pixie cut was all gray.

"Must be love at first sight," she said.

"What'd you do to yourself?"

"Sorry, pal." She patted my shoulder. "You're not exactly my type. I play for the other team, remember?"

"The Old Gray Mares?"

Katie gave me a sisterly shove.

"Nope. The Silver Foxes."

I spun a tray on my finger like a basketball. "You're, what, late-twenties?"

"A gentleman never asks a lady her age."

"I'll try to remember that if I ever run into one."

She chuckled and backhanded me in the gut. "You're in section three today, numbnuts. A two-top's being sat as we speak. Move your ass."

After a hot shower that evening, I wiped a strip of mirror and gazed at myself for far too long. I could still see the real me behind that emerging mask of crows' feet, eye bags, and permanent laugh lines. What got me the most, though, was my hair. I couldn't explain why, especially since most guys my age suffered major hairline recession, or worse still, bald patches on the crowns of their heads. Maybe the years were starting to show, but I still had a full head of hair, and it was thicker than ever. What did I have to complain about?

Later that night, just as I was pulling together some dinner, I heard a thump at the door. I opened, bowl in hand, to find my neighbor Bodhi leaning against the doorframe, backlit by the setting sun. He wore baggy shorts, a Mexican poncho, and flip-flops, and he was redolent of sandalwood and purple kush. His long blond hair was pulled back in a ponytail. Plus, that grin. He came off like a goofy stoner, and he smoked more weed than anyone I knew, but there was something else to him, something more profound. I couldn't put my finger on it. Wisdom, maybe. If he hadn't fallen bass-ackwards into an acting career, you might mistake him for a guru.

"Smells good, bro."

"Hungry?" I said through a mouthful but didn't wait for an answer. I pushed the door open and wandered to the couch. "Help yourself."

Not two minutes later, Bodhi brought a bowl of stir-fried veggies and noodles in from the kitchen, lounged back in the La-Z-Boy, and put the footrest up. "Righteous," he said while gnawing on carrots and onions and red bell peppers.

We ate in silence for a while. After we cleaned up the last of the bamboo shoots and ginger, chopsticks rattling in empty bowls, we leaned back into the cushions.

"When you're eating," said Bodhi, "just eat." He'd already started rolling a joint.

"And when you're smoking," I said, striking my Zippo and lighting those aromatic herbs, "just smoke."

We sank into that herbaceous cloud for a while.

"Something different about you," I said, passing the spliff.

He grinned. "Like it?"

"What's *it*?"

Bodhi untied his mane and shook out who-knew-what onto my rug. His blond locks cascaded to his shoulders. Only they weren't blond anymore.

"Not you, too."

"Looks rad, right?"

I shook my head. "Why does everyone suddenly want to go gray?"

"Naw, bro. Uh-uh. Not gray."

"I'm sitting right here, Bodhi. I can see it with my own two eyes."

He took another drag. As he exhaled, he said, "Illusion is not real: who is right, who is wrong? The unreal is not actual: what is empty, what exists? Thus I realize that attainment gains nothing, and loss loses nothing."

"That's deep." I was higher than I'd intended. "But if it's not gray, what is it?"

"One word, bro." He grinned. "*Silver.*"

"You're joking, right?"

He shook his head, laughing.

"What's the difference?"

"Dude, look at it." He shook it back and forth as if he was in a hair-care commercial. "It's hella shiny."

"Gray—"

"Don't even say it."

"Can be shiny."

"Not a chance."

I chuckled. "What about metallic gray paint jobs?"

"Now you're talking gas guzzlers? Planet polluters? Do you even hear yourself?"

"This isn't climate change, Bodhi, it's—"

"*Silver.*"

We sat in silence for a long moment.

"Still," I said, "it looks gray to me."

Bodhi gave me that inscrutable grin. "The fool who persists in his folly will become wise."

I slept through my alarm the next day and only woke up when Katie called to berate me. I knew she needed me too much to follow through on her threats, but I was still in a tizzy, half-dressed and unwashed, as I wheeled my bike into the late-morning glare. Bodhi sat on his porch, shirtless, an unlit joint between his fingers. His girlfriend Mila leaned against him, half-asleep. She was long and lithe and a pretty well-known actress. She'd died her hair gray, too.

"'Sup, dude," he said. "Early start?"

I shook my head. "Late as always."

"Bummer."

I dug in my pocket for my Zippo. "Need a light?"

His clear blue eyes gazed right through me. "When the

sickness is healed, what is the need to cling to the medicine?"

I flicked it a couple times, then put it away.

He grinned and said, "You need a better job, bro."

"Tell me about it."

"No, for real. Something's come open on the show. Perfect for you."

I wheeled my bike over. "The show? As in—"

"*Every Rose.*"

I hadn't acted since I played a gas station attendant in the indie classic *Long Gone Goodbye*. That was longer ago than I cared to admit. "What is it?"

He chuckled. "Maybe it's not that artsy-fartsy stuff you're into. Steady paying gig, though. Legit cash, too."

I checked the time: I was still running late. "What kind of role?"

He shook his shiny silver locks. "Erica will fill you in."

"Who's—"

"Casting director."

I was having trouble keeping up.

"Audition, dude. Tomorrow."

"No way."

He lifted both hands from his knees, palms up. "On the level."

"Should I prep something, or—?"

Bodhi waved away the suggestion like ganja smoke. A pod of cyclists rolled past. The sun peeked out from a slit in the clouds.

"Thanks, Bodhi."

"No worries, bro. Just bring your A-game, okay?"

When I finally made it to Ensō, Katie lit into me the second I was through the door, railing about schedules and responsibility and setting a bad example. Maybe she was just showboating for the rest of the staff, as everyone in the kitchen, prep cooks, expediters, and waiters, acted busy but hung on every word. Still, she had a point.

"Sorry," I said. "It couldn't be helped."

"My ass."

"Is perfect."

"Don't give me that," she said, dragging me into her office. She slammed the door, then almost smiled. "Seriously, you're making me look bad, Jimbo. Can you please get here on time? And wear a less-wrinkled shirt? And stink a little less of weed?"

I blinked and opened my eyes wide for her to inspect. "How red are they?"

"Not bad."

I nodded, organizing my apron. "Listen, Katie, something big's come my way."

"Yeah?"

"An acting job. Real money."

"Good on you."

"Heard of *Every Rose*?"

Katie snickered. "Tell me you're not serious."

"Why is that funny?"

She rolled her eyes and eased back into the kitchen, absently wiping a spotless prep station. Kitchen staff scurried to look busy.

"Not a TV fan?" I asked.

She scowled, studying the section assignments. "You're in three again today. Hungry customers await."

I peeked into the main dining room. "There are maybe six tables."

"And two of them are yours, smartass. Better hustle."

On a typical shift, I was a well-oiled machine, but today nothing went right. Calamari mix-ups and spilled chardonnay were just the beginning. I couldn't get the timing down, so I left a four-top gnawing bread and sipping water for half an hour but served a pair of businesswomen their entrees when they'd barely started their appetizer. When four attorneys got drunk on midday sake, only to stiff me, I had to go out back and scream into a dumpster to keep from getting fired on the spot.

Then, right before my shift ended, a white-haired lady at Table Three started giving me the eye. The woman's daughter, probably in her mid-thirties, was blathering at her when I brought the check, but it was clear she wasn't listening. The woman grasped my wrist in her bony hand and said, "You look pretty good for your age."

Was that supposed to be a compliment?

"Perhaps you and your sister here would care for an espresso and chocolate mousse?"

The lady tittered. Her daughter faked a smile and grabbed the check. "Nope," she said, "that's it."

They paid in cash and left a miserly tip.

Later, as I clocked out, Katie studied me with a pinched expression.

"Sorry about today," I said. "I'll bounce back tomorrow."

"You're not on—"

"You're telling me."

"No, tomorrow. You're not working."

I pondered for a moment, remembering the audition.

Katie shook her head. "What happened to you, Jimmy?"

I puzzled.

"You used to have standards."

"Who said anything about art? It's an acting gig."

"On a cheesy-ass soap opera."

"It's not that bad." I'd never even seen it.

"Right, it's *awful*. Next thing I know, you'll be getting Botoxed and face-lifted and hair-dyed."

I forced a laugh. "Don't worry so much. It's just an audition."

Katie sighed. "Okay, Jimbo. Break a leg."

When I got home, I slammed inside, leaned my bike against the wall, and dropped my messenger bag. *You look pretty good for your age*. It stuck in my craw. The Manly Man box hadn't moved from the counter next to the sink. In the mirror, I looked

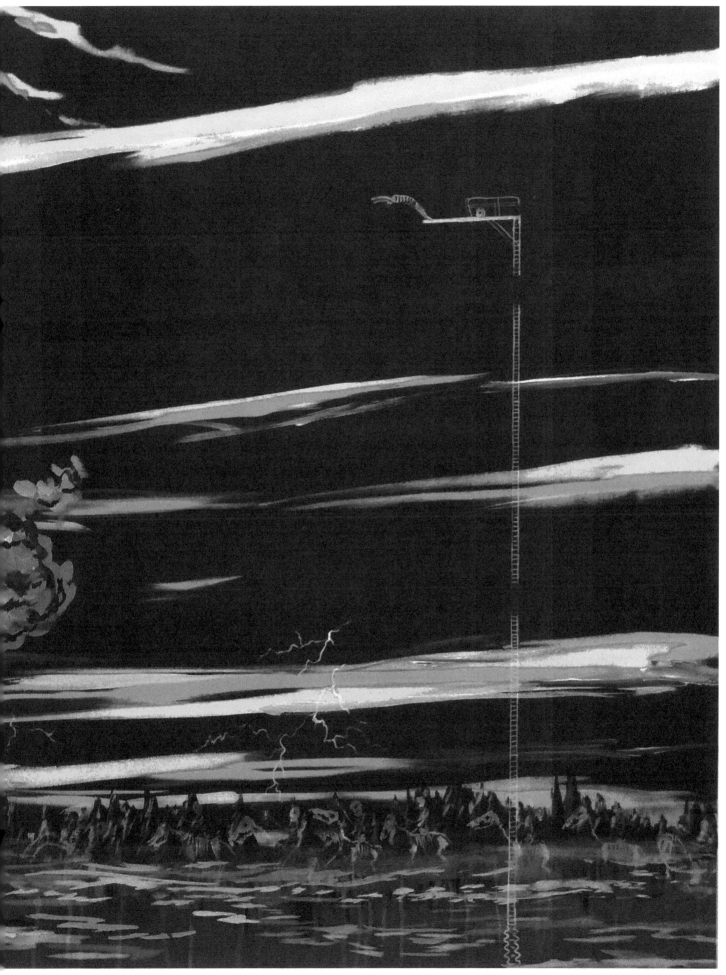

even more worn out than I felt. My hair seemed thinner and saltier—who was I kidding?—*grayer*. I picked up the Manly Man Comb-In Color and scanned the instructions. Then, without flinching, I opened the box and went to work.

That evening, I locked my bike outside a new food-cart pod, then slipped through the gate. My younger sister Zoe stood in the amber glow of twinkly lights strung over a courtyard filled with picnic tables. Face in her phone, she didn't spot me until it was too late. I grabbed her by the shoulders and shouted, "Gimme all your money!" She had a slight build and spent more on her nails than she paid in rent, so I wasn't expecting an elbow to the gut and a fist to the chin. "Hands off, motherfucker!" she yelled. Next thing I knew, she'd wrenched my arm and flipped me through the air onto my back. The gravel thud knocked the wind out of me.

I blinked and gasped. Zoe leaned over me, a bottle of pepper spray aimed at my face. Her face looked strange from this angle, pinched and a little orange. "Jimmy?" she said.

As I struggled for breath, I smiled and gave a little wave. Concerned patrons wandered back to their banh mi and vegan vindaloo.

"You're getting slow in your old age," said Zoe, helping me up.

"Someone can't take a joke," I wheezed. But did I mean her or me?

We milled for a moment. Zoe scanned her phone and talked about the self-defense classes she'd been taking, while I explored the dinner options. Meatless barbecue, Indian, and wood-fired pizza, Turkish, Peruvian, and Mexican. I opted for a jackfruit sandwich and curly fries. Zoe went for vegan lomo saltado. It was BYOB, so I uncorked a decent bottle of pinot that'd survived the body slam and poured.

As our plastic glasses clacked, I finally noticed her hair. It was long and full as ever, only now it was gray.

"What did you do?"

Zoe gazed back at me, eyes wide. "You took the words right out of my mouth."

We guzzled wine and refilled our glasses.

"You look ridiculous," we said in unison.

"You don't like it?" she said.

"What's wrong with it?" I asked.

"It's unnatural."

"Speak for yourself."

I dug into my jackfruit sandwich, and Zoe fiddled with her sauteed veggies and tempeh as a stream of hungry folks arrived by bicycle, scooter, and streetcar. The silence between us didn't bother me: I knew it wouldn't last long.

"It's just that," said Zoe, wiping her mouth with a paper napkin, "you looked good before."

"I looked old."

"You looked authentic. Natural. Rugged."

"Do you plan to let your hair go gray?"

She stabbed at her dinner with a plastic fork. "It's different for men. It looks distinguished."

"So what, you sped up the process?"

She shook her head. "It's *silver*, Jimmy. There's a difference." I scoffed.

"What's that supposed to mean?"

"Nothing. Bodhi. He embraced the granny look, too."

"I love that guy." She took a sip of wine, then wiped off the lipstick smear. "He got me a part on that soap thing he's in. I'm playing this hot, young maid Thorn falls for."

I didn't have a clue who Thorn was, but I nodded over my pinot. "That's great, Zo."

I polished off my jackfruit and fries, while Zoe nibbled at her meal. Peanut oil and ozone filled the air. Other tables emptied, only to fill again. I gazed around absently, counting heads of dyed gray hair. There were so many, I gave up. Soon I said:

"Bodhi's found something for me, too. Audition's tomorrow."

She forked a chunk of tempeh and studied it in the amber light. "Then you better do something about that hair. You look like a used car salesman."

"Lay off, okay? I'm rolling back the clock."

"Seriously, Jimmy. Don't show up tomorrow looking like that, okay?"

"You'll get used to it. We all will."

"Trust me, big bro. You'll regret it."

After dinner, I took a different route home. When I hit the park, I slid out of the saddle and walked my bike. Street lights flickered and hummed on the perimeter, but not ten yards down the path, the darkness thickened. No wonder, given those towering hemlocks and firs, yews and sequoias. I could barely see three feet in front of me. I inched forward, slipping in muddy patches and stumbling over roots.

That's when I saw the glow. At first, I thought it was someone's headlamp from afar, a patchouli-scented mycologist or enterprising vagrant. As I approached, though, I realized it couldn't be human: it was too low to the ground, too quick and fluid. I stopped, peering into that pure silver light. The shine was so intense I had to shield my eyes, yet a strange peace washed over me.

Then I spotted him. He resembled a small dog, though with a slender face, pointed ears, and a long, bushy tail. He smelled of sandalwood and sunlight and studied me with icy blue eyes. That peaceful feeling deepened.

"Wu wei," he said.

I felt my eyes widen. "Excuse me?"

"Effortless action."

"Right, go with the flow. Don't try too hard." Then it hit me: "Wait, you can talk?"

"To use words but rarely is to be natural."

"Huh," I said, stupefied.

The fox gazed up at me, alert, curious. His steady glow lit the park for twenty yards in every direction, casting the trunks of oaks and maples in clear silver light.

"So, like, do you live here?"

He padded a few steps toward me. "Living in the world yet not forming attachments to the dust of the world is the true Zen way."

I laughed and wagged my head. "You sound just like my friend Bodhi."

The silver fox watched me in silence. A smile glimmered behind his eyes.

"Do you have any, I don't know, words of wisdom for me?"

He gave me a pensive look. "Willows are green and flowers are red."

"Uh, okay?"

"Bamboos are straight and pine trees are gnarled."

I shifted my weight, Chuck Taylors crunching in the gravel. Silver light pulsed and glowed. I realized we stood in almost complete silence, nothing audible but a slight breeze soughing through the evergreens. That sandalwood smell mingled with earthy loam and pungent sap.

"That's it?"

His gaze grew more intense, a blue-eyed silver swirl. "All worldly pursuits have but one unavoidable and inevitable end, which is sorrow: acquisitions end in dispersion; buildings, in destruction; meetings in separation; births, in death."

I blinked and rubbed my eyes. "That's depressing as hell."

"Life is short, the time of death uncertain."

I waited for the rest. He offered more of his steady gaze, then drifted away.

"Wait a second," I said. "Is that really what you're gonna leave me with?"

He wandered a few more steps away. His light dimmed until I could make out little more than his blue eyes. "Much speech leads inevitably to silence. Better to hold fast to the void."

Then, just like that, he was gone.

My audition was the next morning. I thought I'd be up all night, but I slept like a dead man. When I woke, I was clear, alert, relaxed. Rain drummed on the roof. I scrubbed my face and ran a razor across my chin, admiring my youthful appearance in the mirror. The Manly Man had taken off at least ten years.

I made a strong pot of coffee. When I sat down at the rickety kitchen table, I found a note from Bodhi. "Tomorrow at 11. Stumptown Studios. So stoked, bro!" He didn't have a key, so how'd he get in?

Rain thrummed against the living room windows, and when I peeked through the blinds, the sky was a low, gray canopy. Cars hissed down the boulevard a block away. A woman walked with her little boy up the sidewalk past my building, and he splashed with both feet into every puddle he came across. That used to be me: where had the time gone? As I stood there, watching

the rain come down, I assured myself that spring showers never lasted long.

As I brushed my teeth, I checked my hair in the mirror. It still looked great. When I was dressed—nothing fancy, just jeans and a black t-shirt—I threw on my rain jacket and messenger bag, then wheeled my bike out the front door into the wet, gray morning. The steady rain had slackened to drizzle.

Traffic zipped along the wet asphalt. Somehow, I avoided getting splashed, much less run down, by pickups, panel trucks, and taxis. I pushed across the highway overpass and cycled half a dozen more blocks before another shower cut loose. It rained hard for five minutes, then stopped right as I located Stumptown Studios, an old red brick warehouse. I locked my bike to a light pole and brushed off the rain, then I was through the door.

The vibe was minimalist chic. High ceilings, exposed beams and trusses, huge windows through which poured gray spring light. I wandered over to an enormous wooden reception desk that appeared to be floating three inches off the polished concrete floor. The girl standing behind it smiled beneath her beanie. I wondered if the hair it was hiding was gray.

I told her why I was there. She gave me a funny look but nodded, checking something on her tablet, the only thing on the desk.

"I'll let them know you're here." There was that look again. "Can I get you anything to drink? Sparkling water, espresso, chai?"

"I'm fine," I said, overplaying a grin. "Where should I—?"

"Wherever you feel most comfortable."

I wandered toward the windows. There were no chairs, not even uncomfortable, ultra-minimalist ones. I had just settled onto the cold concrete when she said:

"The restrooms are just down that hall. In case you need to"—she mimed washing her face—"freshen up before your meeting."

I could take a hint. The door was marked with a complicated symbol I assumed meant all genders. I stepped inside, expecting to see my face splattered with road grime. Instead, I found dark stains running down my cheeks and neck. My first thought was, *Blood?* Then I realized:

Manly Man Comb-In Color.

I grabbed fistfuls of paper towels and began sopping it up as it ran down the collar of my shirt. The rivulets left a brown residue that took serious scrubbing to remove. Trouble was, as soon as I'd get everything under control, more would run down my face and neck. I needed to stop the flow at the source, and that meant toweling out my hair. I pulled the lever eight or ten times, ripped off a long sheet of paper, and gave myself a good working over. When the towel soaked through, I repeated the procedure. It took three or four tries before I'd mopped up all the moisture. The towels turned so dark they were almost black. My hands, too.

When I checked myself in the mirror, the situation was worse than I'd feared. All the color washed out, so I was back to square one. I wadded up the stained paper towels and pitched them into the trash. Then I scrubbed the gunk off my hands and raked my hair into place.

The receptionist looked expectant as I skulked up. "They're ready for you now."

"Great," I said. But I was back to salt-and-pepper, so what was the point?

She led me through a doorless doorway on the wall twenty feet behind her, then down a short corridor and into a steel-and-glass atrium. Sunlight streamed through the roof. Two women and a man perched around one corner of a sleek conference table ten yards long. I assumed they were the casting director, director, and producer of *Every Rose*. Apart from their matching hoodies, I didn't notice anything but their hair: it was all gray, cinderblock to cathedral.

One of the women gestured toward a leather chair. "Have a seat."

After that point, the audition was mostly a blur. I may have read from the *Every Rose* script. They surely told me about the role, though I only learned the details later. They wanted me to play Rip, a sexy, older gentleman and father of the show's protagonist, Thorn—acted by none other than Bodhi himself, though he and I were only a couple of years apart. All I really remembered from the meeting itself, though, was the three of them gushing about me.

"Isn't he perfect?" said one woman.

"Bodhi said he'd be perfect!" said the other.

The man nodded like a bobblehead. "I can't believe it."

"Look at that hair," the first woman said.

"Luscious," said the second woman.

The man kept nodding. "It's Rip in the flesh."

They tried to hire me right then and there. Maybe I'd only ever played bit parts, but I knew better than to ink a contract on the spot. Still, it sounded promising. I told them I would give it some thought and get back in touch soon.

As I pedaled home, I marveled at the sun playing hide-and-seek behind the clouds. The streets were only damp in patches, and traffic seemed thinner than usual. I felt younger than I had in years.

Then, all at once, I was at the park, Douglas firs and redwoods towering into the urban sky. I glided to the sidewalk, then dismounted and walked my bike along the same path I'd taken the night before. Don't ask me why. Maybe I was riding a high, or maybe I felt at peace with the world. More likely, though, I was looking for that silver fox.

I wandered around the wooded trails, scanning the forest, peering under bushes, freezing at the slightest rustle, ears pricked, eyes searching. Passersby gave me funny looks and a wide berth. Yet all I spotted were blue jays, crows, and a few red squirrels—nothing that even resembled that silver fox. When I reached the south end of the park, I considered doubling back and giving it another shot, but somehow it all felt forced. I was trying too hard. So I let it go.

Just as I was about to hop back on my bike and pedal home, an old pickup honked, then eased to the curb. Mila sat behind the wheel. Bodhi grinned out the open passenger window.

"How'd it go?" he said.

We bumped fists. Something smelled like french fries.

"Not bad."

"Gonna take the part?"

"I don't know. Yeah, probably. We'll see."

"Beats the hell outta slinging hash, right?" His blue eyes shone. His silver hair shimmered in the sunshine.

"What's with the truck?" I asked.

"Belongs to Mila."

She beamed me a lovely smile.

"Bio-fuel, bro. Wave of the future."

I nodded. "That smell's making me hungry." I noticed a mound of wetsuits and half a dozen surfboards strapped down in the bed. "Starting a surf camp?"

Bodhi tucked a strand of silver hair behind his ear. "Big swell's coming, dude."

"Right on."

Blue jays flitted from branch to branch, singing their song.

"You should come," said Bodhi.

"But I don't even—"

He wiped away my words, his gaze a blue-eyed silver swirl. "Life is short, bro. The time of death uncertain." Now he pushed open the door and slid over to make room for me. "You in?"

I grinned, hoisting my bike into the truck bed and climbing into the cab. "Wu wei," I said.

"Effortless action," said Bodhi.

We grinned at each other. Then Mila released the break, and we glided away into the silver afternoon. ◐

Cute Meat Does Portland

KOURTNEY PARANTEAU (she/her) (aka Cute Meat) has worked in some of the finest and most notable restaurants in Portland and Los Angeles. Her cookbook memoir, tentatively titled *Cute Meat Does Portland*, is coming out late 2023. We asked her about a few of her favorite Portland food joints, and she answered with recipes.

www.cutemeatinc.com

In Da Clerb Sandwich

Serves 4 people, easily (it's a lot of sandwich)

Like a go-to karaoke song or television show rewatched over and over, getting to know someone's favorite sandwich is a glimpse into their psyche, a peek inside their adolescence, and can act like a cheat code to their heart. Personally, I'm always ready to karaoke Selena Gomez's "Love You Like a Love Song"; recite dialogue from *Buffy the Vampire Slayer*; and a California club tops my sandwich list.

Portland's best club sandwich exists at one of the city's most beloved diners, the Cameo Cafe. It's lovely and disjointed (in the best way), and visually more aligned with San Luis Opisbo's Madonna Inn than an old school diner. Cameo Cafe boasts the only dining room in town where Paris Hilton would fit right in amongst its pinks-of-all-shades decor, and ornate, frilly accents. A lesson in maximalism upon entry, even if I'm not really hungry, I'm drawn to the undeniable optimism of Cameo's dining room.

Their club sandwich is a classic rendition with ham, turkey, and bacon; a stack of meat I don't think I've ever enjoyed with company. Instead, I've eaten it with a book, a side of fries, and a Diet Coke every time I visit. My version is a sandwich that aims at the heart of a classic club but omits ham, replaces it with avocado, and asks the preparer to make a simple, herby pesto to spread on the toasted bread for a bit of spring/summer ambiance.

Ingredients:

For the parsley dill pesto:
1 cup parsley, roughly chopped
¼ cup dill, roughly chopped
¼ cup high-quality olive oil
8 oz spreadable goat cheese
½ cup unsalted pistachios
2 teaspoons kosher salt
1 teaspoon black pepper
2 teaspoons freshly squeezed lemon juice

For sandwich:
12 slices shoku pan bread (a Japanese milk bread known for its fluffiness), lightly toasted

24 slices cooked bacon
12 slices of turkey breast
2 tablespoons Kewpie mayonnaise (a Japanese brand that is creamier than its　　American competitors by virtue of utilizing only the yolk of eggs)
2 tablespoons yellow mustard
12 slices of sharp cheddar cheese
2 red heirloom tomatoes, sliced into medallions
2 perfectly ripe avocados, sliced into crescents
8 long sandwich toothpicks

In a food processor (or blender if you don't have one) blend the pesto ingredients slowly until the greens are broken up but still in distinguishable flecks. Each sandwich, because of its substantiality, will house three slices of toasted bread. On the interior side, spread a generous layer of mayonnaise on two slices (the bottom and top of the sandwich). On their mirroring middle slice, spread one with yellow mustard and the other with your herby pesto.

Between two slices of bread on the lower-level, stack bacon and avocado; on the upper-level, stack tomatoes, turkey, and cheddar cheese. Repeat for the remaining three sandwiches and cut diagonally before piercing each triangle with a toothpick to hold the sandwich together. Serve with crispy potato chips.

Skirt Steak with Mushrooms

Serves 2

There's no way in hell I'll attempt to mimic the signature dish served every night of the week at Clyde's Prime Rib. It's one of Portland's oldest mainstays and the only restaurant in town that offers tall, clamshell, leather booths associated with old school Los Angeles restaurants. While not everything is fantastic at Clyde's (stick to the basics), their Louie salad, shrimp cocktail, side mushrooms, and strip steak all are worth ordering when you're not in the mood for a slab of bloody prime rib (which I am every month on the first day of my period). My wink at the restaurant that's seen me in lipstick most often is just a simple hybridization of their two most slept-on great dishes, the aforementioned side mushrooms, and simple skirt steak.

Ingredients:

Skirt steak, brought to room temperature, 1½ lbs
2 teaspoons kosher salt
2 teaspoons black pepper
2 tablespoons unsalted butter, separated
1 large shallot, minced

2 cups shiitake mushrooms, all sliced in half
½ cup red vermouth (like Dolin) (also known as sweet vermouth)
1 tablespoon capers
3 stalks of chives, sliced thin

As you pat dry your steak and coat it in salt and pepper, melt butter in a pan over medium-high heat (making sure to bring your steak to room temperature, drying, and seasoning before it hits the pan will help ensure the meat gets a crispy crust). Being mindful not to splatter yourself with butter, gently but quickly place the steak in your pan and cook for two minutes per side. Pull cooked steak from pan and allow to rest undisturbed on a plate.

Returning to your pan, lower the heat to medium, and melt your shallots in the remaining butter until their fragrance takes over the room (about four minutes). Toss in your shiitake mushrooms and cook for two minutes until they lose a little of their structure. Simmer your buttery mushrooms in vermouth for three minutes or until the alcohol cooks out, and remove from heat.

Coming back to your steak, slice the meat against the grain into bite-sized pieces and plate. Spoon the mushrooms over the steak and finish with capers and chives before serving.

PNW-oise Salad

Serves 6 as a side salad and 2 as a main course

My best recipes are the ones I write as an ode to one of my people. As a friend, I've often been (rightfully) criticized for taking up too much of the room's energy, and for acting selfishly, but most of all, my best friends have pointed out how bad I am at initiating hugs. I'm trying to improve on all of the above (mostly the hugging, the other two are really hard), but this recipe is a hug to a friend who has made my life more comfortable over the past decade.

So many restaurants and cafes in Portland are dotted with mental diary entries where I've eaten and gossiped and giggled with Maya Attar, and at the top of the list is Sweedeedee. In the past, I've been somewhat agnostic about the daytime hotspot, but in recent months I've come around and seen why so many of our city dwellers feel drawn to their wooden booths. The first meal I remember falling for was their Niçoise salad. My version is specifically tethered to the bounty of the PNW, the people I feed inside it, and hugs to Maya.

Ingredients:

For the salad:
Raw salmon, 1½ lbs
1 tablespoon sunflower oil
2 teaspoons paprika
2 teaspoons kosher salt
1 teaspoon black pepper
3 medium-boiled eggs (about 6 ½ minutes in boiling water), shelled and cut in two
1 cup artichoke hearts in liquid
6 asparagus stalks, shaved and blanched (boiled for around 3 minutes), and chilled
2 cups fingerling potatoes, boiled and halved (boiled for around 25 minutes), and chilled
2 heads of butter lettuce
2 tablespoons capers
1 tablespoon sliced chives
2 slices of day-old focaccia, toasted and smashed into breadcrumbs
Zest from one lemon
2 teaspoons bottarga (a delicious, salty fish roe) (optional)

For the dressing:
½ cup high-quality olive oil
¼ cup sherry vinegar
2 tablespoons honey
2 teaspoons mustard seeds
1 teaspoon celery seed
2 tablespoons lemon juice
1 teaspoon fennel seed, crushed or roughly chopped
2 teaspoons black pepper
1 tablespoon dill, finely chopped
1 teaspoon tarragon, finely chopped
2 teaspoons kosher salt

In a cast iron skillet, heat sunflower oil over medium-high heat until glistening. In the meantime, pat your salmon dry with a paper towel before rubbing it evenly with paprika, salt, and pepper. Skin side up, cook the salmon for three and a half minutes without jostling or disrupting. If your pan begins to smoke, slightly lower the heat. Flip salmon so the skin is now kissing the cast iron, and cook for an additional two minutes before removing. Allow to rest on clean paper towels.

As your salmon cools, whisk all of your dressing ingredients together in a small bowl, set aside, and also toss your breadcrumbs, bottarga, and lemon zest in a separate small bowl. Again, set aside.

In a large mixing bowl, toss butter lettuce with a tablespoon of your dressing, and set the greens on a large serving plate (one that's just a little bit bigger than you think you'll need. Plating a dinner salad like a Niçoise isn't unlike arranging a bouquet. You want each element visible but none of them too outshining). Find a zone for your potatoes, artichoke hearts, and asparagus in opposing corners of your serving platter before gently breaking up your hunk of cooked salmon, setting it over the bed of lettuce and other greens. Finally, arrange your egg halves over the salad, sprinkle capers, breadcrumb mixture, and chives evenly over the entire salad.

Trout Almondine

Serves 2

Luce on East Burnside serves a radiatore with fennel, saffron, and lamb that is amongst Portland's finest dishes. It's spiced in a way that reminds me of being in a fancy sauna, the flavors mingling to create a unique eucalyptus-like essence. Made perfect accompanied by a bottle of briney Vermentino, this recipe is a love note to my favorite place to kill a bottle of wine.

Eliminating the pasta and meat but incorporating the fennel and saffron, this is an easy almondine fit for a weeknight dinner.

Ingredients:

Trout filet, 1½ lbs
2 teaspoons neutral oil (like sunflower, grapeseed, or vegetable)
2 teaspoons kosher salt
2 teaspoons sweet paprika
¼ cup all-purpose flour
½ cup unsalted butter, at room temperature
2 cloves garlic, finely chopped

Juice from ½ a lemon
½ cup dry vermouth (like Dolin)
¼ cup finely chopped parsley, plus more for garnish
2 teaspoons saffron threads
1 teaspoon fennel seeds, crushed or roughly chopped
1 cup almond slivers

Heat oil in a frying pan over medium-high heat. As the oil comes to temperature, pat your trout dry with a paper towel, sprinkle with kosher salt, paprika, and dust with a thin layer of flour. When your pan glistens with heated oil, gently place your fish (skin side down) in your pan and cook for three to four minutes before flipping and cooking for an additional three minutes. Remove your fish from the pan, and lower the heat to medium.

Melt your butter in the pan seasoned with fish fat, and cook garlic until fragrant (about three minutes). As the butter begins to brown, cook your parsley and add your saffron, fennel, and salt to the mixture while stirring continuously with a wooden spoon. After a minute, drizzle vermouth over the mixture, and cook until the alcohol has reduced (about three minutes). Finally, add the lemon and almonds, and cook for an additional four minutes. Let the sauce simmer over low heat while you plate your trout. Over the center of your fish, spoon over the almondine. Garnish with parsley and serve. ⓑ

THE UNITED STATES OF AMERICA

I-797A | NOTICE OF ACTION | DEPARTMENT OF HOMELAND SECURITY
U.S. CITIZENSHIP AND IMMIGRATION SERVICES

Receipt Number
WAC212785115

Received Date
07/07/2021

Notice Date
02/24/2022

PORTLAND

2024

The above petiti...
valid as indicate...
petition and duri...
file a new Form

The dates in the
of up to 10 days
L-1B, O-1, O-2,
and 30 days after
The decision to g
contact the IRS w

The petitioner sh
right part (the I-9
Protection when
visa-exempt mus
required, he or sh
or pre-flight insp
notify a consulat

The approval of t
abroad and seekir

Please see the add
USCIS encourag
www.uscis.gov/fil

California Service
U.S. CITIZENSH
P.O. Box 30111
Laguna Niguel CA

USCIS Contact C

...assification is
...detailed in the
...y require you to

...n a grace period
...2B, H-3, L-1A,
...e week before
...orized by law.
...appeal. Please

...should keep the
...ms and Border
...e U.S. and is not
...a. If a visa is not
...at a port of entry
...request that we

...States (if traveling

Detach This Half for Personal Records

Receipt#
I-94#

672085307 56

Receipt Number
US Citizenship and Immigration Services

'Try Harder' Collage by Yuyang Zhang

28

Bad Memory

Essay: SCOTT KORB (he/him)

Scott Korb is the director of the Pacific University MFA in Writing program. He lives in Portland.

Photography: SYLVIE HUHN (she/her)

Sylvie's work often touches on climate anxiety, urban deconstruction/reconstruction vs. natural habitat, and archival memory. Using mixed media, she methodically builds the surfaces of her paintings with layers including printed ephemera, found objects, and fragments of personal photo-transfers – information she could never retain because of a learning disability that affects her short-term working memory. Dealing with her learning disability is a battle Sylvie has embraced. She has a Masters in Library Science, with a concentration in archives.

www.sylviedakotahuhn.com
@sylviedakota

Traveling among farmers and naturalists in the Pacific Northwest over the summer of 2019, I noticed in myself, for a time, what seemed a remarkable sense of recall. Maybe my mind was sharpened by the fresh air and food, the bracing swims in the lake, the presence of a fearsome bald eagle. Perhaps the responsible neurons were sparked by the presence of old growth Douglas firs or the different rest offered by the night's quiet. But in conversation around the kitchen's central butcherblock, or seated on the deck of a guest house in preserved forests of western Oregon, words and whole concepts came to mind and spread out before me in ways I found surprising. Certain things were just there for me to say, so I said them.

The subjects I spoke about with ease and confidence weren't new to me; no, I wasn't conjuring new knowledge in those moments but doing what I suppose we all always do during good conversation: remembering something we once committed to memory and adding it to the mix of whatever else is being said around us. Whatever it is the others are remembering. Some of this is storytelling, tales drawn from our lives that we often tell and retell. At its best—at our best—some other part of conversation involves insights we hope are useful, direct and indirect challenges to notions presented by others, questions that might prompt new clarity, maybe even a *bon mot*. Sometimes we poke fun. All of this seemed available to me on those summer days and nights in the midst of these friends. New things came of that admixture, no doubt—but it wasn't the newness of what we were all able to say that captured my attention. In those moments it wasn't what bubbled up among us that was most impressive to me, even as we talked, and even as I took pleasure in the company. (This is not how I like to behave around friends. It's sometimes been said that I'm a good listener.) What most impressed itself upon me was that, at the time, I felt somehow possessed of my own memory, as if my memory and I were one.

I don't recall now—of course—what specific words and concepts I experienced such sudden fluency with over those weeks: we were often talking about organic agriculture and a local, orphaned raven, high-level high school baseball and, for an evening, walruses. Nor do I believe I showed my amazement with seeming to know, at every turn, what I knew. But I took mental note: I hadn't remembered being able to remember this well.

Exhilarating as it felt, as I consider it now, my experience over those days distresses me a little. After all, what's made clear when I look back on that flush of wholeness is that typically—say, as I write and try to remember that summer in this moment—I'm unwhole, dispossessed of my memory, estranged from it in ways that I'm not sure I've ever realized. I've forgotten lots of things lots of times, but I haven't, until now, understood how

fundamental forgetting is to my experience of engaging with others, or even, to use a phrase whose aptness feels suddenly stunning, sitting by myself. That is, sitting at the side or edge of myself. Or, in the vicinity of myself. Near, close to, or beside myself.

I suppose I'm not so different than anyone else in these terms. And maybe everyone else already knows this about themselves and about me. Maybe most people manage their forgetfulness less existentially. Maybe it's no big deal, and I should take heart in the possibility that as part of my typical internal estrangement, I'm probably more open to others, less aware and so less concerned with my own prowess as a rememberer.

But still, I remember thinking in the midst of one of those conversations: Is this what it's like to feel smart?

There's a story from my life that I never tell. Near the end of summer, 2007, I traveled to Italy to spend time with my fiancée, an artist who had spent months leading a painting course in Tuscany. Teaching with her over those months was a handsome and talented marble sculptor. You see where this is going. Where it went.

That's the story. During our travels, there were pasta and seafood dinners, I recall a train station and the marble shop—I helped this man move marble—and a harrowing bus ride along a steep coastal road of what might have been Naples. A friend recently told my wife and me about a trip she'd taken to Naples and I couldn't say whether I'd ever been there, so I didn't say anything at all about Italy. Again, I never do.

In the notes I've taken over the years to write this essay, I have something scratched down about how I might gain more insight into the end of my engagement if I consider it in light of a phone call I received, a few years later, from a friend seeking advice about the dissolution of his marriage. During this phone call, he raised the question of kids, a house, family, Tahoe, none of which, in the midst of my breakup, did I have to think about. In the summer of 2007, I had none of the things my friend was concerned with—no home, no kids, no extended family, no Tahoe. No, I moved out of the apartment I shared with my fiancée, stayed in friends' places until I found a studio to live in, and before long got a dog to help with the grief, I suppose. The dog then became my wife's dog, too, our son's dog, and then, finally, our son's first great grief.

The insight I thought I might glean by comparing my loss with my friend's loss has something to do with how gutted I felt when the relationship ended, and what a gutting might feel like now—now that I do have a kid, now that I am married—with so much more at stake. How could the loss of love be worse than

it was when that relationship ended? With extended family, a child, it would have to be worse now, I thought in the wake of that phone call, than it was in the summer of 2007.

And I'm obviously right. That's the obvious insight. I hardly have any memory at all of those weeks—was it weeks? mere days?—in Italy, or of the loneliness and shame of not being a rock sculptor. Losing what my friend lost, all that I've gained since summer 2007, is unthinkable: my wife, our home, our son.

But what about Tahoe? My notes say "kids, house, family, Tahoe," but I cannot recall, looking back, what my friend meant. He was probably talking about ski vacations, maybe a second home. I don't know. But here's the worst thing: I also don't remember who this person was who called me. Who was I talking to? Whose life, whose suffering, was supposed to have

given me deeper insight into my own life and suffering, such as it was, and such as it would be if my marriage were somehow to fall apart? This is not how I like to behave around friends, but I can't remember.

After traveling in the Pacific Northwest and then through National Parks in western California, we ended our summer in 2019 on a beach near San Diego where we have often gone to relax, a place that just this morning my wife recalled with such fondness that it made us wonder what we're doing with our lives. One day, while our son was in the waves, my wife pointed out a flying machine that she believed at first might have been a glider. There are cliffs overlooking this beach, and perhaps, she thought, it had been launched from there. I recognized the machine and I knew it wasn't a glider, so I tried to tell her what it was called, but I couldn't recall.

A few days later, I tried to remember again by writing about it. I asked her for a pen and began scribbling on the final blank page of a collection of short stories I'd just finished. This is what I wrote:

> I'm thinking of a word that has three parts. It's a word I feel like I've forgotten before—like *shallot* is a word I've forgotten before, staring into our pantry drawer and looking at a vegetable (is a shallot a vegetable?) I cannot name. The word with three parts I'm thinking of now—I can't recall now—is the name of a flying contraption I saw in the middle of the summer, on a Southern California beach (the same beach where I'm writing this, and within just a few days). I saw these machines as a child and I knew their name then, but I also probably forgot their name then for the first time.

> If I don't remember the name of the flying machine by the end of this essay, I'll look it up. But they are single-passenger flyers, not enclosed, but open. They take off from land, though my wife, at this beach, wondered if this was so, because there are high cliffs in this town where this flyer may have launched from. What is the word? Shallot? I want to say *hydro-*something, but that's not right—it's not a water vehicle and in my childhood I was nowhere near a beach, or not very often. I'm writing to try to remember.

Here's where I put down the pen and walked on a large rock at the beach, glancing into the surf—eyeing my son—then up at the sky as some clouds rolled in. Then I wrote:

I think it's called an ultra-light.

I remembered.

"It's called an ultralight," I said.

"What is?" she said.

I know people who fret about losing their memories. People who, in their own middle age, say, would worry upon looking into the pantry, seeing a shallot, and wondering, *What is this thing called again?* Perhaps these people more often feel more *oneness* with what they remember, more like I did those days around the butcherblock and under the Oregon firs, less estranged from themselves—provided it's plausible what I'm

saying: that what humans know somehow establishes who we individually are. Perhaps these people stumble less over their words and feel smart most of the time.

For a time, I wondered whether my wife is one of these people, a worrier. She tells me, in this way, she's not—though what led me to ask is that each morning she fills in the crossword on her phone and scribbles solutions to a Mensa-puzzle calendar, all before getting out of bed. "A soccer game ended in a 2-2 draw. How many possible different half-time scores were there?" (Answer: 9.) Some days she does two crosswords.

The research conflicts on whether puzzles like these, done in our relative youth, will stave off mental decline or dementia when we're old, but one recent study indicates that the sort of problem solving my wife enjoys may provide "an individual with a higher cognitive point from which to decline." That's not nothing.

My own genes suggest that I might benefit from taking up this puzzling—raising the cognitive point from which I'll decline, if I've not already begun—just like I've taken up the daily yoga my wife introduced me to several years ago and which keeps me relatively flexible, in body and mind. My mother has the memory lapses typical of people in their seventies. I think she always knows what a shallot is. But she misplaces things, forgets she's told me something, repeats a thing she's told me. I don't worry that much about my mother in this regard. Her mother's memory, however, particularly that mechanism mapping the short-term, has basically expired, and has been declining this way for more than a decade. In recent years, for those who care for her, my grandmother's memory has become maddening (as often happens for caregivers). Her activities are limited, she rarely leaves the house and has taken some falls. Someone needs to be with her. And the person with my grandmother, which has often been my mother, must contend with her not knowing the things she's recently been told or things she's experienced. Twenty-four-hour news suits her, made, it seems, for people who need constant reminding.

Yet, there are faint echoes in her. Her daughter Mary Beth, another of her caretakers, recently died. Her illness must have felt sudden, if, in the day-to-day, with a hospice worker in the home they shared, my grandmother was aware of her slipping away at all. In the mornings after her daughter died, my grandmother would report feeling very sad though not be able to say quite why. Someone would have to remind her, "It's Mary Beth, Mom," and that explained it, at least, we hoped, until the following morning.

When she greets my wife she always asks, "Doesn't your father live in England?" And she's right, he does.

She also knows about the increasingly distant past—her late husband, the houses they built together, the family they raised, the move from suburban Milwaukee to north-central Florida in the early Sixties, her career in hospitality, the death of their son Ted, the death of my father. She remembers my father, his marriage to my mother, how after he died, in a crash some 200 miles away, her house in Sarasota was abuzz with people. My mother and sister and I were with my grandparents there on the Gulf Coast; my father and my brother were spending a few days with relatives in Gainesville. That's where the crash took place, near Gainesville, just outside of Jonesville. My brother lived and my father did not. My grandmother still knows this, that her eldest daughter was widowed that day.

I can't help it that this is where this thinking about memory and estrangement has been going; when I sit down, by myself, to try to remember, this is where my thinking very often goes. And then, this is one of those stories I tell and retell, the one I tell and retell the most.

When I ask my mother about the time—the days, the weeks, even the year—after my father died, she tells me she can't remember anything. My brother and I had counseling, and so did she, but she doesn't recall what it was like or who she met with. (I recall, of my therapy, learning the word "cope" and also a large white room with risers, where we played; I recall more vividly the hallways and elevators of the college where my father taught computers, and where I also played.) I've been told that after my brother was released from the hospital my mother would, in the evenings, go to bed immediately after she closed our bedroom door for the night, and though I don't recall who told me, word must have originally come from her, but again, she doesn't recall. My mother remarried a few years later, and perhaps that's where the memories pick up again. Together we can recall her wedding, the dances I did, the cake, her dress, the hall.

When we are around people we are often around—those we love and spend our lives with—there's the tendency to qualify the retelling of certain stories in conversation. I'm sure we did this during our time in the Pacific Northwest that summer. *Kate's heard me tell this story a million times*, I'll say. The qualifications we offer to these stories can seem at first like an apology to the ones we love and spend our lives with—*sorry, hon*, she'll seem to say, *but you have to hear me recall once again the time my father sent me away, at twelve, on a barge trip to Amsterdam, when the permission form listed fourteen as the minimum age and most of the girls were even older than that…* Or, from me, *sorry, love, that you have to hear me recall once again the time, while biking in my early thirties, I made a spiderweb of a cab's*

windshield after the driver slammed into me late one night on Delancey Street.

But just as often we'll say to one another, in a group—*tell them about the time your dad sent you off to Amsterdam, on a barge. Tell them about the time you ended up at Bellevue Hospital, with a likely concussion, reciting your Social Security number to that woman you used to date.* So, at least in my experience, the apologies aren't usually really apologies, because the stories exist as part of the texture of our lives together. We need the stories like we need each other, because, in a way, those stories—those memories, told and retold—are what makes up the other person. Losing them seems unthinkable.

But, then, maybe what we're really doing when we issue those qualifiers is to keep at bay those days we all know are coming, and sometimes already come, when those we love and spend our lives with hear us begin a story and then interrupt: *Sorry, hon, you've told me this already. Sorry, love, don't you remember?*

To finish the thought, we suppose the worst is yet to come, when we don't even tell each other we're covering old ground, but the listener bears the old story and turns to someone else he loves and spends his life with, and whispers, *Dad's telling the same old story about the cab again.*

Or is this really the worst—the same old story?

There is a line from French book I've liked, probably because it spoke to me in a certain way, that says, in English, "other people's memories gave us a place in the world." I'm not sure when I first read this line that I grasped just how consequential the memories of other people could be. Being at the side or edge of other people. Or, in the vicinity of those we love and spend our lives with. Near, close to, or beside them—even when they're maddening. I'm not sure I've understood until just now that losing those memories, shared as the texture of a life together, could threaten one's own place in the world— far more, perhaps, than coming to grips with the fundamental place forgetting has in our lives. It's what happened to my mother just outside of Jonesville, a version of which I perhaps felt in what might have been Naples. This must be what my friend meant when he worried about Tahoe. What I couldn't understand then. And it's funny, I remember who he is now, this friend, now that I'm done. ⓑ

33

Stuffed Rabbit

WHEN I WAS FIFTEEN, MY BOY-
FRIEND GAVE ME A TEDDY BEAR,
AND I FELT WEIRD ABOUT IT.

ON A NIGHT SOON AFTER, I WAS
HANGING OUT IN A PARKING LOT
WITH A DRUNK FRIEND.

A WOMAN GOT OUT OF HER CAR
WITH A BUILD-A-BEAR BOX.

YOU'RE TELLING ME
YOU _BUILT_ THAT BEAR?!

THIS MUNDANE BUSINESS CONCEPT
WAS REVELATORY WHEN PRE-
SENTED TO A DRUNK TEENAGER.

Comic: LIZ YERBY (they/them)

Liz Yerby is a non-fiction cartoonist based out of Portland, OR. They were recently nominated for an Ignatz for Outstanding Story for *Big Cats* which discusses queer figures in history who owned exotic cats, as well as their own experiences with tigers. They are also known for diary comics and their peanuts fan-fiction. Their work can be found at ***lizyerby.com***.

Oregon Grown

What it's really like to grow weed—before and after legalization.

In many ways, it feels like cannabis in Portland is old news. Since Oregon voters approved Measure 91 to legalize cannabis in 2014, brands have risen and shut down; gotten acquired by Canadian investment firms and spread to multistate empires. Cannabis cups and pot parties have ebbed and flowed, impacted by indoor air regulations and COVID-19. Following the spike in sales when cannabis was deemed essential during the pandemic, consumers' shopping habits have steadied, much to the concerns of the small businesses riding a steep plunge in prices. The Green Rush that many associated with the legalization of cannabis has turned out to be a pretty rocky ride, and since the spotlight has moved to other states legalizing the plant, the realities of growing cannabis in Oregon have slimmed to a dismal stream of headlines about theft, struggle with tax burdens and oversupply. But that's only one part of the picture.

No one has better insight into the inner workings of this world than the growers that grew before Oregon legalized cannabis and continue to grow today.

Nelson and Co. Organics, High Noon Cultivation, LUVLI and LOWD are four examples of boutique grow operations working within the licensed recreational program. These farms have stood the test of time, law enforcement, and the cutthroat environment of a severely saturated market to make the transition from legacy to legal. To capture a clearer picture of Portland cannabis, past and present, I asked each cultivator to share what stands out about the old pre-legalization days and the new days since. The good; the bad — the memories that feel a lifetime away — as well as what makes the challenging day-to-day of doing things legally worth it.

Foreword & Interviews: LAUREN YOSHIKO (she/her)

When Oregon legalized adult-use cannabis in 2014, Lauren Yoshiko was writing cannabis columns under a pen name at *Willamette Week*. Since then, her coverage of the commercial and cultural happenings in the industry has appeared in *Broccoli Magazine*, *Thrillist*, *Conde Nast* and *Rolling Stone*.

Photos: CHRISTINE DONG (she/her)

Christine Dong is a Vietnamese-American photographer documenting the many shapes of the human experience through food, family, and culture. Dong lives in Portland, OR with her camera and two canines.

christinedong.com

Greg Levine, co-founder of Nelson and Company Organics with Mike Ciarlo. Growing since 1996; recreationally licensed since 2017.

BEFORE:

I came out to the West Coast in the early '90s because of weed and music. I could find the things I liked out here, and people who liked the same things. We were really fortunate to meet people that led to getting our hands on really prized varieties of weed that we still grow today.

Growers were our only friends, because they had to be. You could only open up so much to people pre-legalization, and you wouldn't ever think of inviting them over. There's risk in any house sitter stealing your plants or worse, notifying authorities. It's just what happens—our Chem 91 cut is definitely from some kid who was watching another grower's property while he was away and stole a bunch of cuts while he was there.

Music is what led to finding most of my longest-running strains, because concerts were just where you met like-minded people. Everyone still went to concerts back then, for one, and then conversations start when joints are getting passed around. I can't remember exactly which shows led to which strains, but I'm pretty sure I met Mike at a String Cheese Incident show. Now, you search online, you call someone, and you buy genetics. Very different.

AFTER:

My life changed drastically when I was able to tell my parents what I did for the first time. I did not tell them until I actually received the approved OLCC license, in hand. It really freed me as a person. If I didn't have to lie to my parents anymore, I didn't have to lie to anyone ever again. I could do whatever I wanted.

If I'd never gone legal, I'd still be just as proud of the work I do, but a lot more secretive and weird about society. It's tough because you get a little lost, not trusting anyone. Always looking over your shoulder and worrying about abstract possibilities that are never going to happen—it can be isolating. Now, I can go out to lunch with my son and I don't have to worry about reeking of weed when I get there, and neither does he. We're still very much owner operators—Mike and I pull off most of the labor between the two of us. That's what we want though. We're young enough, and I don't know what else I'd do.

Janeen Sandvig, co-founder of High Noon Cultivation with her partner, Tyson Lewis. Growing since 2003; recreationally licensed since 2016.

BEFORE:

I'm a third-generation grower. My paternal grandmother grew—and got arrested for it—and then my mom grew my whole life. She used my diaper bag to hold the baggies when she did deliveries. The culture was so different back then, and I do miss the sense of the safety net we had. Yes, there was a constant state of fear of your door coming off the hinges and everything being taken from you—your crop, your home, your car, your livelihood, your freedom— but if something happened, you knew who to call and that they'd pick up no matter what. The women looked out for each other. All my babysitters were growers, because my mom couldn't drop me off with just anyone. When I got older, I had this network of people to reach out to for seeds and cuts to get my own grow going.

I have fond memories of the trim parties during harvest season. One time, I remember one of the growers really wanted to produce a whole video about growing cannabis—this is like, late 1980s—but they wanted to protect everyone's identities, so everyone had a paper bag on their head. So funny and creepy. Actually, one of my main babysitters, Patty—her dog ran into the frame at some point, so she never let them release it.

AFTER:

Getting this piece of property to live and grow on, buying out our partner, expanding to New Mexico—this feels incredible, and would've been a lot scarier and harder to do underground. I still stutter when people ask me what I do, but that's just that enduring stigma from all the propaganda we've all been exposed to for so long.

I was originally studying pre-med while at university, and I was working in a nursing home at that time, seeing all those prescriptions, it was so hard, knowing what my mom did and seeing who she helped and how happy they were, versus these walking zombies at the nursing home. It really reframed how I understood what cannabis does to and for people. I felt like my mom helped so many people through weed, and this made me question how much I'd help people if I continued down the path of studying conventional medicine. Now, that feels truer than ever. As a mom of soon-to-be four kids, I can say that for me, cannabis has been essential as a parent.

Tim Zimmerman, co-founder of LUVLI. Growing since 2001; recreationally licensed since 2017.

BEFORE:

There was a local task force in the early-mid 2000s that targeted home grows in Oregon and Washington with these things called "knock-and-talks." One time I was helping a buddy trim at his house, and a man and a woman came by saying they were from the Sierra Club, asking us to sign an environmental petition. The only reason we answered the door was because we were waiting on someone on their way to help trim. The next day, my buddy spotted a surveillance van on that street, and he ended up going to jail.

It got to the point where if we noticed our trash cans got messed with on garbage night, we'd do a full tear down overnight. We'd put everything—plants, lights, pots, all of it—in contractor bags, and toss it in a Uhaul. We got really good at taking down and setting up rooms, and really creative with the growing tools. I rigged a timer for lights with an old water heater; we built our own 240-volt outlets. We didn't risk running HVAC, because it would be a suspicious thing to see on the outside of a regular house. You always wanted to keep your house looking really nice in general, because you didn't want to bring attention from your neighbors. Had to make time to mow the lawn and plant flowers. Definitely weird times.

AFTER:

I can do my job better today, with way more tools than I had doing things before. The old days were so much shooting in the dark and having to just invent solutions. There was no Google University. Now, we can go out and talk to people with more expertise and actually get help. We don't have to be afraid to ask questions and be open about what we're doing. Companies don't have to be afraid to touch cannabis growing technology anymore either, and majorly overdue innovation is happening.

It makes me feel old, but I get excited when I think about the next generation of growers—the people who don't even know they're interested in growing yet, but will be. They have access to all these tools; they won't be held back by the same paranoia from pre-legalization. It's cool to think about what weed could be like ten years from now, once the new generation gets to really explore it, way more openly than we were able to.

EVERYDAY I'M HUSTLIN'

Jesce Horton, founder of LOWD.
Growing since 2013; recreationally licensed since 2020.

BEFORE:

I am originally from Virginia, and then lived all over—Florida, Atlanta, Germany. I never tried growing until I moved to Oregon. I was scared, I'd been arrested for having one seed on me in Florida. I wasn't even planning on growing, we just had shitty weed out there. It'd probably fallen out of a bud in my pocket months prior.

When I lived in Munich, I spent a lot of time in Amsterdam, and that feeling of not doing anything wrong when you're smoking cannabis was intoxicating. Moving to Oregon was its own dose of that—getting a card and getting to just go shop for weed at a neighborhood store. Then I found out that I could grow it at home, and I was like, if I can, why not try? I picked up a clone of Black Cherry Cheesecake, got a basement grow going, and just never stopped refining and expanding from there.

During that medical window prior to recreational, it was different. Growers weren't competing in the same way for licenses or eligible real estate. Everyone was sort of doing their own thing, and we'd share genetics in the community. I was a new arrival here and it was no time before fellow growers, shop owners, and consumers were sharing knowledge with me to get my grow going. Cannabis culture, to some degree, always connects people. Growers; consumers — a lot of us like the same music, watch the same stuff, use the same lingo. Cannabis unifies.

AFTER:

In cannabis, a lot of the culture is closely entwined with how I grew up; with Black culture. As the industry becomes more mainstream, a lot of that heritage is being changed, erased, or reconfigured. LOWD is vibrant and out there and celebratory of that culture, and everyone who really loves weed. People who smoke like they grow it, whether or not they do. And people have responded to it; they want to support us.

That's what excites me more than anything: the true will of consumers matches the industry we want. They want a diverse, ethical industry; they want to see companies like us grow. As I got going, people supported me, and now, I've got a team I'm supporting at LOWD—I'm hoping that true spirit of our cannabis community stays strong moving forward. As we pass through each of these toll gates towards normalization and federal legalization, we have to be sure to carry the important parts we want to maintain with us. ⓑ

The Day I Quit Instacart

Flash Fiction: TRACEY NGUYEN (she/they)

Tracey Nguyen is a Vietnamese-American poet and founder of
Fruition Dried Fruit.

Tempting, the aquarium. It's a complete jargon fest, but I will say this: more than five of my nails are broken and it's embarrassing. Kick me, kiss me. I have been kissed but never kicked. Today I made negative twenty dollars. But we have chicken tenders and milkshakes. It feels so good to stretch out and just lay there. And just move you know? Maybe I have been kicked, by accident. Or just fell? Kicked by gravity and something on the ground. What was on the ground? Anyway, I'm grown up. Literally. I can do anything! Anything! I was running around downtown and waiting for teeth man and parking too far away because the one ways and short stretches to streetlights stress me. Unwieldy traffic, unyielding drivers. So I park far, walk, like my mom says to do. And forget to pay for parking. There's an app for it though. It charges twenty cents. Jaw clenched, back clenched. I am probably shrinking

A Bear, A Possum, and Two Girls Walk Into A Strip Club

Story: MICHELLE RUIZ KEIL (she/her)

Michelle Ruiz Keil is an author, playwright, and tarot reader with an eye for the enchanted and way with animals. She is the author of the critically acclaimed young adult novels *All of Us With Wings* and *Summer In The City of Roses* which is a finalist for the inaugural Ursula K. Le Guin award for Fiction. Her writing for adults can be found most recently in *Bitch, Cosmonauts Avenue,* and the anthology *Dispatches From Anarres.* Michelle has lived in Portland, Oregon for many years where she curates the fairytale reading series All Kinds of Fur.

Illustrations: TOMÁS OLIVERAS (he/they/she)

Tomás Oliveras is a 30-year-old QPOC illustrator working primarily in marker portraits, as well as mini polymer clay sculptures. A self-taught artist, his work reflects the controlled chaos of his methods, straying from traditional portraiture into the world of the surreal. Each piece is created with the intention to both soothe and disturb, capturing the extremity of the subject's gaze, leaving viewers wondering, *what the hell are they staring at?*
@tomatosita

I.

Once, two girls lived in a condominium complex bordering a vacant lot. They shared clothes, rode matching banana-seat bicycles, and slept in identically laid-out bedrooms with windows facing one another across the parking lot.

Summers, they were together all day, on the phone all night. Mornings were chores. Afternoons were roller skates and soap operas. At five, they started dinner, first in one kitchen, then the other.

At six, their mothers arrived home from secretary jobs in the city. Freed from their suits and control-top stockings you could see how young the mothers were. Makeup off, you could see how tired. After dinner, there might be fighting. Later, when the moon rose, someone usually cried. Mother, daughter. You couldn't tell which.

By sixth grade, the girls were called Neve-and-Rosa, never Rosa-and-Neve. They stopped holding hands in public and could no longer share each other's clothes. Rosa's bra size surpassed her mother's, then Neve's mother's. Her jeans size was next. At that time, in that place, smaller was always better. Tiny Neve in her ballerina training bra was the winner while Rosa continued to lose. She was the first to sprout underarm hair and acne. The first to get her period by two whole years.

Before, adults had cooed over Rosa's waist-length curls and long, dark lashes. Other girls said, "You look like Tiger Lily in Peter Pan," and begged for a turn to brush her hair at recess.

Neve was the pretty one now, odd-eyed—one hazel, one

blue—with toast gold hair and skin as pale as paper. She ruled the middle school until she tired of it. Sometimes, she was mean, ditching Rosa for other girls or dropping her apple core into Rosa's milkshake at lunch. Rosa knew she snuck out to see boys at night but kept it to herself. Neve needed her secrets.

In high school, Neve got straight A's and dated college guys. Rosa barely passed her classes and was the lead in all the school plays.

Enter the bear. Rosa met him one night at rehearsal.

"So, are you, like, a Grizzly?" she'd asked.

"Kamchatka."

Rosa looked him up and down. Yellow-eyed. Tallish but slender. "A bit small for that, aren't you?"

"We're slow to mature," said the Bear. "I'll fill out in the end."

His name was Alexander.

He read nonfiction and played piano. Chopin, Schubert. Difficult pieces. For listening, he liked industrial music that sounded like the insides of ships.

Rosa and the bear spent time together after rehearsal, eating at the all-night diner or smoking weed in the playground of the abandoned elementary school. On weekends when Neve had schoolwork or a new college boy, Rosa and the bear went to the movies in the city, black and white arthouse films with subtitles and impenetrable plots. They did not hold hands but the space between their velvet seats was electric. Rosa knew that if they kissed, something big would happen. Something that changed them.

In the weeks that followed, Neve was suddenly boy-free and Rosa saw less of the bear. One Saturday evening, the girls were alone in Rosa's apartment. Both mothers were away for the weekend with thickset, mustachioed men. Rain beat against the windows, *jealous of us,* Rosa thought. Neve handed Rosa a whiskied Dr. Pepper on ice.

Then the bear came knocking. He was on Rosa's doormat, had come with intentions toward her, but when he saw Neve, that was that.

"Your eyes," he said. "Like David Bowie's."

Neve said nothing. She didn't have to.

The talk turned to math and music theory. Neve brought out her chessboard. There was nothing for Rosa to say. It was a game she did not know. Not bothering with her shoes or jacket, Rosa ran barefoot across the parking lot to Neve's unlocked condominium. Inside, she burrowed into Neve's bed and slept until Neve found her at dawn.

II.

Rosa is a city girl now with an apartment of her own. For money, she dances.

"A dancing bear," says Alex.

"No," Rosa says. "That's still you."

Alex belongs to Rosa, a hand-me-down like the half-burned candles and butterfly sheets Neve gave her when she packed for college. There was no place for them in the dorms, she'd said. Just like her relationship with Alex. And he'd agreed. They parted friends. What Alex and Rosa are doing is not cheating. Still, neither Alex nor Rosa has told Neve about this development.

Now it's winter break and Neve is visiting. Planning to stay a few days with Rosa. Alex heads for his dad's. "Good luck," he says, kissing the top of Rosa's head.

The apartment is a mess. Rosa hides the evidence as best she can, shoving Alex's dirty clothes under the bed and his telltale snack food in the cupboard over the refrigerator, but in the end, she confesses. She cries. Neve rushes to the bathroom. The water runs for a long time.

When Neve returns her eyes are red-rimmed and muddy. Her lips are bright as blood. She puts on music, a mix she made for the drive from her college town to Rosa's city. She sits on the sofa next to Rosa.

Neve grabs Rosa's long ponytail and pulls. Sometimes, when they were kids, Neve tested Rosa this way. She looks like she did then, her face very still, focused on some private experiment whose parameters Rosa can't know.

But then Neve leans in. Kisses Rosa on the mouth. Gently. The softness a contrast to the burn on her scalp as Neve keeps her hair pulled taut. Her free hand shoots under Rosa's dress, past her underwear, deep inside.

Rosa's eyes widen. Shock and pleasure.

Mouth to mouth Rosa can't breathe. Doesn't want to.

It's like she and Neve are in one of the bear's foreign films, moving through a riveting story that makes little sense. They do everything. Or Neve does. Rosa wants to give Neve her turn under the waterfall of familiar hands. The shock and pleasure of

a long-loved mouth. But Neve won't have it. She holds Rosa's wrists as she moves above her, sex to sex, taking pleasure herself in the end.

After that, they sleep.

Without a word, Neve leaves at sunrise.

Rosa lays in bed all day watching the curtains move across the open window.

III.

Neve invites Rosa to visit her at college where she's dating a professor old enough to be her dad. After the bookstore, thrifting, and dinner Neve leaves to sleep at the professor's house. His wife is finally out of town. "I'll be back for brunch," she says.

Abandoned in Neve's single dorm, alone in Neve's narrow bed, Rosa rolls on her stomach, replaying the night they were together. She comes so fast. Does it again. Tries to sleep. Thinks about Alex.

He writes to both Neve and Rosa now—a power move they cancel out by reading the letters to each other over the phone. Still, there are things in Alex's letters Rosa holds back. Neve is sure to do the same.

Rosa gets up, opens a drawer. Neve's diary. There's something in back. A shoebox. The letters? Neve's mother was a phone-call listener, a purse violator. After eighteen years of surveillance, snooping is the one transgression Neve can't brook.

Rosa resists the shoebox, gets dressed, and walks to town for junk food.

Neve is at the convenience store buying a bottle of water.

"Here," Neve says, like she expected Rosa all along. She holds out a small square of paper. "Stick out your tongue."

Rosa obeys. The acid zings. Her taste buds tighten.

"What happened?" she asks. "Why are you here?"

"He was putting a crib together when I got there," Neve says as Rosa pays for her Diet Coke and Hostess Cherry Pie. "For the new wife."

"The new wife is a baby?" Neve snorts. Rosa links her pinkie with Neve's.

"The acid was stashed in his toolbox. I said he should get rid of it. Kids get into everything."

They walk into the forest behind campus. The breathing trees are familiar from other trips in other forests. But deeper in, firs turns to Redwoods. These, with their buffalo coats and sweet wet perfume amplify whatever the acid is starting to do to their brains. Rosa kneels and pushes her hands into the forest floor. She lays down, cheek to dirt. Neve sits with her back to a tree. Soon, they're laughing, not caring that it's starting to rain.

Neve explains atoms and molecules to Rosa using raindrop trails as visual aids. Webs appear between them, mandalas of water and starlight.

The sky clears. They wander into a clearing that becomes a quiet neighborhood of newly built houses.

"Look." Neve pulls a crumpled fifty-dollar bill from her back pocket. "He gave me this."

"Like, a tip?"

"He said cab fare."

"Are there even cabs in this town?"

"Exactly."

They sit on a curb. Water seeps through Rosa's jeans. Even tripping, Neve remembers to take off her raincoat and spread it on the wet pavement first.

"Do you think about that night at your apartment?" Neve is looking down, doing Origami with the fifty-dollar bill.

"I thought it was off-limits. A one-time thing."

"I never said that."

Rosa laughs, her face distorting. "Am I wrong?"

"No," Neve says, folding and unfolding the bill. "I just wonder. What do you think about it?"

"I try not to," Rosa says. Even on acid, she doesn't say why.

"So that's it?" Neve's eyes meet hers.

She wants something. Rosa casts around for a crumb to feed her. Something to deflect attention from the truth of it. How often she thinks of that night. How much she wants to repeat it.

"I dance to your mix now," she says. "Every shift. My tips have tripled."

Neve puts the swan-folded fifty in her pocket. Her eyes are all pupil. "I'm not used to being jealous of you."

"Uh, Neve? You're pre-med with straight A's and I'm a stripper taking acting classes in a city that's not New York. Whose scene work is solid but never auditions."

This last part is something her acting teacher says to her often. It wah-wahs in her brain for a while. Frying. That's what Alex calls tripping on acid. An odd word.

"What are you thinking about?" says Neve.

Us Rosa thinks. Then says, "Remember when we watched that movie?"

Neve nods.

That movie is the *Story of O*, an adaptation of the infamous French S&M book aired on late-night softcore cable. Were they thirteen? Fourteen? It was at Neve's house. They were sprawled on the sofa, Neve's cold feet tucked under Rosa's warm thigh. Time stopped when the first sex scene came on. For Rosa anyway. She'd laughed to break the moment, shoving Neve's feet away like they were gross. She suggested they turn the movie off. But no, Neve wanted to finish it. They did in silence. The images hung between them for weeks.

"Did you feel almost like…I don't know. What if we'd kissed? What if we'd fooled around?"

"No," Neve says. "Oh my god. You were my only friend. It would have been too weird."

"And it wasn't too weird last winter when you put your hand in my underwear?"

"That was different," Neve says. "I was mad."

The acid crashes into Rosa's brain, a sleeper wave. She thought they'd peaked in the forest but Neve's eyes are drained of color and her hair is crackly with static, haloing her head.

"I wanted us to be even." Neve says.

"Even with who?" Rosa's words are rubbery. They bounce off the minivan across the street and land back in Rosa's mouth. The rain starts again.

"You stole my boyfriend," Neve says, twisting her silver thumb ring. "You like it when I lose."

"I like it when you're human."

"Fuck you," Neve says.

Tears roll down Rosa's face.

Or maybe it's the rain.

IV.

This time, Alex quit school and moved in for real. Neve is visiting for the weekend staying on their sofa.

"Their" sofa. "Their" apartment—even though it's Rosa who pays the rent. The story is he'll pay her back. Soon, he'll turn twenty-one and that means money. Alex is a trust-fund bear. Until then, there are bills and someone has to pay them. Rosa is already two weeks behind for her acting class. So she is going to work and Neve is going to the party with Alex in her place.

The three of them getting ready has an odd okay quality. Neve, always quick to dress and put on her no-makeup makeup, strums Alex's guitar while Alex does his eyeliner at the closet-door mirror. Rosa dabs the excess coconut oil she'd applied after her shower onto his chapped lips—a normal thing when they are alone. Neve stops playing, watching them.

Rosa freezes in her robe and bare feet, terrified that some cringey boom chicka boom threesome energy will emerge. But Neve turns away and starts a new song on her guitar. An old favorite of Rosa's from an album both their mothers used to play nonstop.

Alex puts on his boots. Rosa stands behind Neve to adjust the straps on the slip dress she's loaned her for the party. The fit is oversized but sexy. The black silk makes Neve even paler. "Like Madame X," Alex says. "Compete with the snooty attitude."

Neve throws a pillow and acts mad, but Rosa knows she doesn't get the reference. Art history is not Neve's thing.

Rosa's cab to work is a no-show so the three of them share, dropping Rosa off first.

In front of the club, tiny hourglass Lupe, leaving at the end of day shift, raises her perfect eyebrows as the taxi drives away.

"That's her?" She knows about Neve and the ponytail. "And your Alex?" She'd met Alex too, out for dinner on Rosa's birthday. "Ten cuidado, mi amor."

It's so nice how Lupe speaks to her in Spanish and never judges Rosa's terrible accent and verb mistakes when she replies.

"No te preocupes," Rosa says, hugging Lupe goodbye.

But Rosa is worried. About Neve and Alex. About money. She scans the audience but there are only suits—the pinstriped patrons of the Barbie Brigade and the cheapskate tracksuit gargoyles, notorious for going commando under their loose-fitting pants.

Rosa's customers wear band tees, thick-framed glasses, and Converse sneakers. They are boyish men. Misfit men, failing men. Men who don't fit in with other men. Favoring Rosa is generous, a rare moment of surplus in their long list of lacks. They are magnanimous about Rosa's curves, the thirty pounds that keep her body from being fashionable. Renoir would have painted her. Botticelli. Or no, Rosa is more of a Gauguin with her high heavy breasts and warm brown skin. Her regulars know things like this: the names of painters, the aesthetics of other eras. In another time that is what Rosa would have been—an artist's model. A muse. As it is, these customers and their preferences allow Rosa to be unconventional with her music and costumes and still make money.

At present, she is in her Storyville stage. It started with a paper-thin free-box nightgown that floated over Rosa's breasts to her feet like a bell-shaped flower. Hair up, cheeks rouged, and there she was—the teen prostitute from the Goodwill postcard Rosa keeps in her bathroom, bought when she was a teenager herself.

It's one of Rosa's powers, finding objects that make no sense in the moment but later prove to be premonitions. Thriftomancy, Alex calls it. For a bear, he is good with words.

Tonight, in her button boots and bloomers, she is washed-out from winter, chilly and wishing for layers. She approaches a little man whose lap she is sure to break.

"Would you like some company?"

His eyes are fixed on the stage and who can blame him. Pilar is bending over to collect her tips. When the stage is empty, the man nods at Rosa and waves a bill in the air. A ten, not a twenty.

She lowers herself lightly onto his lap as the next dancer's song begins. *Pour some sugar.* A reminder. Rosa makes herself smile. This man she would cast as Iago. She decides to make a study of him for an actor in her class who's struggling with the part.

His legs are so short his feet dangle. His bony shins dig into her thighs. He smells like aspirin tastes when it sticks to your tongue. A coarse gray beard covers his shirtfront and ends at his belt buckle. She thinks of the possums who claimed the field behind her old condo, always fighting with her mother's cat.

"What do you call yourself?"

"Calliope."

"Right," he says, like he's offended she didn't give her real name. "So, *Calliope*, why don't we go back to my place and do some blow?"

That's what it is. One of her mother's boyfriends had a similar chemical reek. The good thing about him had been the leftovers—powder-coated baggies with a line or two left thrown in the guest bathroom trash—the place Rosa did her makeup in

the mornings all through high school. He'd wink when she came out. "Better than coffee," he'd say.

The Possum sniffs and moves his clammy paw from her knee to her upper thigh. She takes the appendage and moves it back. It's heavy, every finger weighed down by a tacky ring. She plays with her rope of dollar store pearls until finally, the song ends. Tall Chrissy walks her spectacular legs offstage for a quick change between songs.

"Would you like me to stay?"

The Possum hands her a twenty. Then another. Then one more. The part of Rosa's brain that's grown an adding machine dings. She'll take Neve to brunch someplace with mimosas. They will shop for earrings on the pier.

She shivers and suppresses a yawn. The night before with Neve on the sofa and Rosa and Alex in the big bed had been sleepless. Once, before dawn, she thought she heard Neve crying.

"Come on, *Calliope*. I have nose candy and poppers." It's more a taunt than an offer. Rosa's not going anywhere with him and he knows it.

She smiles her best ingenue smile and says, "Partying with you sounds so fun, but I'm sorry, I can't."

"Oh, I get it," he says. "You have a *boyfriend*." He laughs. His teeth are surprisingly white.

"I do," Rosa says with enough pity to grate.

His pupils dilate. *Will he hit me?* The thought is outlandish, but Rosa stands by it. She owes him one and a half more songs and then she's out of there.

The Possum tightens his grip on Rosa's waist, turning her so her back is facing him—a signal he wants a lap dance. She leans forward, hands braced on the theater seat in front of her, holding herself up with her thigh muscles and the balls of her feet. If there is an erection in the Possum's pants, mercifully Rosa can't feel it. The cold rings dig into her sides. She hadn't noticed they were on both hands. Her quads burn. A song goes by. It's Pepper now, dancing Bachata in a flippy skirt, doing her no-underwear spins.

His breath quickens. The Possum howls.

Is he coming? Eww! Rosa stands up fast.

"My beard!" He yanks Rosa back down to his lap. "Bitch, your cheap ass necklace has my beard."

The bouncer appears. "Sir," he says. "That's enough!" To Rosa, he says, "Are you OK?"

The possum's anger feels like a win. He is red-faced and ridiculous. She slips off her necklace and perches on the arm of the Possum's chair. "Would you bring me a pair of scissors?" she asks the bouncer.

"How about a refund?" The possum's spittle hits Rosa's chest. Once a customer licked a girl. Said she was salty. In the dressing room, they'd debated which customer fluid was worse: spit or cum. Rosa tries to focus on something else but it's not comforting—Alex and Neve at the party.

"Here you go." The bouncer hands Rosa the scissors with a *chop it off* look. Rosa smiles like maybe she will but snips the smallest section of beard possible.

"No refunds," Rosa says. "But you keep this." She hands over the coarse clippings.

The Possum huffs away. Rosa can almost see his naked tail twitching as he goes. She heads for the dressing room. She's done for tonight. She'll ask someone to dance for her in the final rotation and make Neve breakfast at home.

Rosa is waiting for her cab when the Possum swaggers up and hands her a brown bag with a bottle inside.

"To drown your sorrows." He slips something into her hand—a paper bindle dusted with white powder. "To wake you up tomorrow."

"Why?"

"He's cheating on you," the Possum says. "Your musician boyfriend. Ask me how I know."

V.

Rosa goes to the booth for emergency chocolate.

"You break up with that bear?" The DJ hands her a mini-Snickers.

"Probably."

The Possum had been right. Alex and Neve never came home that night. Or the next. On the third morning, Alex came back alone. Rosa was there in her garters and chemise, pin-eyed on the Possum's speed, mascara-streaked and wobbly.

"I'm sorry," Alex said, holding out his hand. She let him fuck her. She still doesn't know why. Something about the no-sleep days of line after line and no food. Something about her mother, gone now to a prosperous suburb in a faraway state. Or maybe none of that.

"Rosa," he said, over and over until he came. She knew it meant nothing. She'd never be enough for him. She'd never be Neve.

"Don't go," she'd said. "Please."

She'd needed to stay home from work for a week until her shoulder healed, scabbed from the rough carpet as she bumped down stair after stair in her underwear, refusing to let go of Neve's duffel as he carried it away with his guitar and backpack.

If a neighbor saw, Rosa won't let herself remember. She's been drinking at night so she can sleep. It only helps a little.

"No offense dude," the DJ says, "but you can do better." He's sweet, her age, and dates Lori, a dancer ten years older. He hands her a fun-sized Almond Joy. Lupe says the same—that Rosa can do better. But she doesn't mean Alex. She understands who Rosa is really mourning.

Out in the audience, Rosa smells cocaine and tequila and there he is, discoing down the aisle like it's Possum Time. The bouncer is on it. Rosa intercepts. "Sorry," she says. "I need him for a second."

In the back row, the Possum holds out a twenty. Rosa waits, hand out. He gives her two more. She sits down next to him. There's no way she's sitting on his lap.

"How?" she says, eyes on Kayla as she crawls down the shaft of the catwalk. Sexy or too sick to stand? Rosa wishes she could tell. "How did you know?"

The Possum chuckles.

"I'm waiting." Rosa says.

"I'm waiting," the Possum mimics.

Before she can stop herself, she reaches over and plucks out a single strand of his beard. "Eat shit and die," she says—something Rosa's mom used to say to the cocaine boyfriend. She gets up to leave.

"Wait! I'm sorry. It's no big thing, okay? I just know things sometimes."

"Whatever." Rosa turns away. She needs to keep working. Her money has been crap for weeks. The customers smell death on her, breakup carrion. She will refresh her lipstick, eat a breath mint, and try again.

"Hey!" The Possum waves a thick stack of cash. "Take this. Go out front and wait for me. I need to take a piss."

"Why would I?" Rosa eyes the money and sees a string of days where she will not have to leave her bed.

"Take it," he says. "You don't have to come with me. That's your choice. But I have a feeling you will."

Outside, waiting for a taxi with the Possum's money in her pocket, everything happens at once.

A Possum-helmed SUV skids around the corner.

Someone calls Rosa's name from across the street. After three months of nothing—Neve!

The Possum honks. A cloud breaks and dumps water on the city. Neve is standing there in the light of the strip club marquee.

"Please, let's talk!"

The Possum revs the huge car's engine. Rosa doesn't think. She just gets in.

And Neve! Neve follows, climbing into the back seat.

There is a clunking sound—a lock engaging.

Rosa reaches for the door handle. It isn't there.

VI.

A fireplace in the corner blazes but the room is cold. Rosa is dizzy, hasn't eaten anything but those two fun-size candy bars for hours.

"I'm going to take a shower," the Possum calls. "You girls make yourselves at home."

A door opens, a shower turns on. Rosa is alone with the Possum's midcentury modern furniture arranged in conversational seating groups around animal skin rugs. And Neve.

"It should be here," she's saying. "It should be right here!"

"What?"

"Rosa! How did we get in here? Where is the door?"

Neve grabs Rosa by the sleeve like she hasn't since fifth grade. They walk the perimeter of the large space crammed with shipping crates and piles of shrink-wrapped gadgets. In the corner is a raised platform for a hulking bed.

They circle the room once, twice, three times, looking for the exit, but there's nothing, only cold walls papered in dull gold.

"Are you sure we came in this way?"

"No," Neve says. "I can't remember."

"Me either," Rosa says. "I wonder if we're underground."

"Don't say that," Neve says. "I swear, if this is some miles-deep murder lair I will freak the fuck out."

"Stop!" Rosa says. "We can figure this out." She grabs Neve's shoulders and shakes them. There is a spark of transgression. Do they touch now? Rosa lets go.

"So," Neve says, "is that skank weasel a guy from your work or what?"

Rosa shakes her head. "Not a weasel,"

The Possum enters in a cloud of steam with a bottle of tequila, wearing tall furry boots, an open silk bathrobe, and nothing else.

There it is Rosa thinks. *His gross naked tail.*

"Oh!" Neve whispers. "I see it now!"

The Possum trots to a plush velvet sectional.

"Let us out of here," Neve says. "Right now."

"You're free to go anytime," he says. "See ya."

"Very funny," Rosa says, playing good cop. "Where's the door?"

"What's your hurry, ladies?" the Possum says, smiling his creepy, fangy smile. "Sit down. Have a drink. Take a load off."

"Why should we do that?" Neve says. "Where the fuck are we?"

"Most girls ask those questions before they get in a stranger's car," says the Possum.

"Except the ones you drug and kidnap." Neve is shaking. She's so scared. Which begs the question—why isn't Rosa?

"Hey," Rosa begins, catching the Possum's small dark eyes. He breaks her gaze and shakes his head. Droplets from his wet hair fall on Rosa's arm. She shivers. *So gross.* Even so, she sits next to him. Neve's eyes go wide. Is she imagining Rosa grinding on the Possum's lap?

"For real," Rosa says. "What's up?" Her tone is gentle, familiar. As if the Possum is the sort of person she socializes with in real life. She senses a small softening. Touches his hand. "You're kind of freaking us out," she says. "Seriously. The car doors. And now no door here? Where are we?"

"Chez moi," he says. "Mi casa su casa."

"Oh my god," Neve says. "Really, dude?" She's standing behind a rust velvet swivel chair, arms crossed tight over her chest, raincoat zipped to her chin.

"That one needs to lighten up," says the Possum and there's a hint of menace in his tone.

Time for Plan B. Except there isn't one.

The Possum kicks back and begins to fondle his dick.

"Eww!" Rosa says, scooting to the far end of the sofa. "Stop!"

"My house, my rules." The Possum shakes his small appendage at them.

Rosa has an instinct. "Your rules suck," she says, channeling her man-hating seventh-grade self.

The Possum is suddenly less flaccid.

Ugh. She's right. She rolls her eyes and makes the universal gesture for *gag me*. And again, a response.

Rosa sighs. He likes the sulky teen act, probably believes it's the real girl behind Rosa's stripper mask. *He's clever*, Rosa realizes, *but not that smart.*

"Come sit by me," she whines to Neve like they're in the middle school cafeteria. Neve doesn't move. Rosa gets up like it's so exhausting and stands in front of Neve telegraphing the plan with her eyes. Glancing back to the Possum, she pulls the zipper of Neve's raincoat down slowly. Neve allows it and lets herself be led to the far side of the sofa.

The Possum begins to wank in earnest.

"Umm, can you please stop masturbating at us?" Rosa says, imagining the snap of a wad of bubble gum.

"Animals use this sort of behavior as a dominance display," Neve says. "That's clearly what this is" Neve looks at the Possum pointedly. "Are we overcompensating for something, perhaps?"

His eyes narrow. "I don't a need a display. I think it's pretty clear who's in charge."

"Really?" Neve says. She turns to Rosa as if the Possum isn't there. "He's trying to gross us out. To provoke us. Then, when we're done barfing all over his tacky-ass sofa, he'll have an excuse to murder us, chop us in tiny pieces, and throw us in the bay."

A sound comes from the Possum's throat. Something like a growl.

Rosa stands quickly and grabs Neve's hand to pull her off the sofa.

"Where do you think you're going?" The Possum is flaccid again. Flaccid and pissed.

"Need to tinkle," Rosa says, channeling the blondest stripper she knows. "Come on, Neve."

The bathroom is all gold-veined mirrors. Distorted girls everywhere "Neve, it's not working," Rosa says. "You have to stop."

"I know." Migraine-prone Neve rubs her temples.. "I know, I know. Your *Teens Gone Wild* thing is better. I just hate him. I want to stomp his disgusting face."

Rosa turns on the tap. There is no hot water but cold feels good on her wrists. She's nauseous now. Scared. But also, it's still sort of like a dream. Not real. No true peril. The bouncers around someplace just itching to toss a guy like this out on his scrawny ass. But that's the thing. They're not on Rosa's turf anymore. They're on his.

"What do you think he wants?" Neve asks, unbuttoning her jeans and sitting on the toilet. By the sound, she'd been holding it for a long time.

"I think he wants a show. Like at the club. He wants us to giggle and drink his tequila and act like everything he says or does is wonderful."

"Does that actually work?" Neve says. "On anyone?"

Rosa sits on the side of the dark red jacuzzi bathtub. "You think he's done this before?"

"I don't know." Neve wipes and flushes and pulls up her pants.

Rosa feels her own headache coming on. She rolls her neck. Puts her cool hands to her hot face. "Can't we gang up on him? He's the size of a crumpled piece of Kleenex."

"What if he has a weapon in the sofa cushions?" Neve washes her hands carefully. "I think we need to get him in the open if we're going to try anything physical." Their eyes meet in the mirror. A second ticks by. Another.

"I'm sorry," Neve says. "About Alex. But you did hurt me first."

"You broke up with him. It didn't seem like stealing. More like… adopting. Foster care for abandoned bears."

Neve fiddles with the items on the counter. A delicate bowl of guest soaps. A vial of French skin serum. A velvet jewelry box.

Rosa unbuttons her jeans. Apparently, they pee together again.

"I'm going out there," Neve says.

VII.

Neve holds court in the living room. She would have made an amazing stripper.

"So," she says, crossing her legs, "where's Mrs. Possum tonight?"

The Possum blanches.

"What's the matter, Gollum," Neve says. "Lose something?"

He narrows his eyes. "I don't know, Bilbo. Did I?"

"Guess we'll have to play a game."

"Give it back," the Possum says.

"Who did it belong to, I wonder?" Neve singsongs. "A lady, perhaps. Someone's blushing bride?"

"GIVE IT BACK!" The Possum looks a little scary with his pointed incisors and furious eyes.

"Aren't you supposed to ask me a riddle?" She nods to Rosa to refill the Possum's tequila.

"How about this?" The Possum downs the tequila and clears his throat. "*Dear Diary, Doctor Ford has to take Viagra to get it up…*" He flaps his naked tail through the fabric of the robe. "Sound familiar? Ask me how I know."

"Stop." Neve says.

"*Dear Diary, Rosa tastes like the pineapple vodka cocktail Mr. Ruel used to make…*"

Wait, Rosa thinks, wishing for a rewind button. *I taste like pineapple?* Her stomach drops. Her brain glitches. Because wait—that's not the most important thing the Possum is saying. It's Mr. Ruel. He taught history at their middle school. Neve babysat his kids for years.

"Shut up!" Neve is trembling. "Where did you get my diary, you creep? How did you get it? Tell me or I'll flush this ring down the toilet like your stupid marriage."

"Ha!" The Possum shouts, air-tallying a point in his own favor.

"Sometimes I just know shit. I can look at a person and see right where the bodies are buried. Know what I mean?"

Rosa looks from Neve to the Possum and back and sees it— Neve does know what the Possum means. She's good at that, too. Finding weak spots. Using them to her advantage. She would make double what Rosa does at the club. Triple.

"I'll answer your question if you answer mine. Where's your wife now? Oh, right—probably married to someone with a normal-sized dick."

The Possum hisses. He makes a show of tying his robe tight and mimes putting on glasses and opening a book. "*Dear diary, Rosa tastes like the pineapple cocktail Mr. Ruel made after school before I let him finger me in the garage.*"

"Wait," Rosa says. "Neve?" But Neve's eyes are fixed on the Possum. Rosa's heart is raw in her chest. Because somehow, some way, what the Possum is saying is true. One look at Neve tells her that much.

Fury bubbles in Rosa's belly. She is hot now. Takes off her sweatshirt. The Possum doesn't even notice. He is locked in battle with Neve.

He clears his throat and goes on. "*The day after Rosa and I had sex I took forty dollars from her underwear drawer, which was how much Mr. Ruel used to pay me for the hour I 'babysat'.*" The Possum does air quotes then continues. "*Sometimes things are so symmetrical.*"

"I didn't," Neve whispers.

"Better check your nose," the Possum says. "It's getting longer."

"Fuck you." Neve sounds like she's about to cry.

"Fuck you back!" The Possum grins. "*Dear Diary,*" he says, his voice higher, more like Neve's, "*Alex calls me every night when Rosa is at work.*"

"Stop!" Neve pulls something out of her pocket—a plain gold ring on a thin gold chain and holds it out. The Possum keeps going, sounding more and more like Neve.

"*He's only with Rosa because she takes care of him. He can't understand how she makes so much money. I mean, her weight.*"

"He's lying!" Neve says. "Rosa, please."

Rosa shakes her head. Neve is the one who's lying. She wraps her arms around her middle.

"*Last weekend when he came to see me, we never even left my room. I don't know what he tells her, but Rosa must know.*" The Possum closes his imaginary book and looks at Neve. "Your move."

Neve is ashen. Rosa closes her eyes. The thing is, she did know. The same way she knows other unknowable things and forgets them. Her childhood dentist. Her mom's ex. Alex cheating and not just with Neve. At work, they talk about it in the dressing room—the things that happen to women and girls. The way those things have fucked them up.

"Enough," Rosa says. She stands over Neve and holds out her hand. "Give it."

For once in her life, Neve obeys. Her hand is shaky. The ring is damp from her sweat.

Rosa slips the ring off the chain, dries it on her t-shirt, and slides it onto her finger. The chain goes in her pocket. The gold band warms her skin, a sensation that burrows deeper, mixing with her body's blood, a red bird that rises to her throat. She opens her mouth to let it out.

"*Dear Diary,*" she says in an accent something like her abuela's. "*I can't stay here anymore. He isn't the man I thought he was. He tricked me. I'm a prisoner. But I will find a way out.*"

The Possum lunges but Neve steps in front of him and pushes him back onto the sofa.

"Ask me what's in my other pocket, fuckhead." She pulls out a straight razor. Rosa would smile but the words are flying out of her mouth almost too quickly to catch.

"*Dear Diary,*" Rosa says. "*I'm writing this in English so when I get away, he will read it and know I hate him or if they find me dead, they will know the truth.*"

The Possum is crying. "She left me," he said. "I let her out and she never came back."

Rosa lets her face go soft the way big dogs do when they want to look nonthreatening to smaller weaker creatures. She approaches the Possum slowly and kneels in front of him. "Open your mouth, sweetie," she says, showing the Possum what she wants him to do, letting him see inside the red cave of her mouth.

The Possum opens up and puts out his pale furred tongue. Rosa sets the ring on it and uses her index finger to push his chin gently until his mouth is closed. She resists the urge to run to the bathroom to wash her hands. Sitting back on her heels, she strokes her own throat to instruct the Possum to swallow. He shakes his head no even as he complies. Rosa can see the ring's impression against his Adam's apple. Then, it's gone.

Eyes wide open, the Possum gasps and then goes deathly still, face rigid, limbs rigor-stiff.

"Is he…" Neve says, paler than ever.

Rosa stands over him, watching very carefully. It's no use. She has to touch him. She chooses the heart over the neck and again presses one finger to the Possum's skin. His chest is bony, almost concave. His skin is warm. Is there a heartbeat? She's not sure. Rosa sighs and comes closer, gingerly pressing her ear to his chest. Nothing again. Then, a beat. A pause, too long. Another beat. The rhythm continues. Rosa stands.

"Not dead," she says. "Just playing."

The girls exhale. The room brightens with the pearled light of early morning.

Neve stands, turning a circle. Pulls Rosa up to see. Windows! And yes, there, where it ought to have been all along, a door! They are in some sort of basement that smells of motor oil and cigarettes. The spell is broken.

VIII.

Newspaper covers the dirty windows, filtering the early morning light. The once glamorous lair is only a dusty storeroom cluttered with junk.

The Possum plays on, motionless and nearly chinless since Neve shaved off his beard with the straight razor. "Flush it," Rosa says about the gross pile of hair.

"With pleasure," Neve says.

When they are alone, Rosa nudges the Possum's matted sheepskin boot with the toe of her sneaker. "Wake up faker."

His eyelids flutter. He stands up fast. Sits down and holds his head, moaning. "Worse than a hangover," he says.

"What is?"

"Dispelled illusions, baby. Glamours gone wrong."

"You're breaking my heart," Rosa says, suddenly noticing her work duffel on the floor next to the sofa.

"Joke's on you," he says, following her gaze. "Look in your bag."

Instead of a wad of cash, there is a roll of valet parking stubs. "Of course," Rosa says. "More bullshit."

Neve comes back from the bathroom. "Don't go in there," she says. "It's beyond disgusting."

"Thanks for clogging up my john," the Possum hisses.

"You're awake," Neve says. "Where's my thank you for the shave? Lucky for you it wasn't closer."

The Possum pats the ratty sofa cushion next to him. "Come back and I'll say a proper thank you."

"In your dreams," Neve says without any heat. She looks very tired.

Rosa's hoodie and Neve's raincoat are hanging on nails by the door. The girls don their layers and Rosa hefts her work bag.

"Smell you later," Rosa says to the Possum.

"Not if I smell you first," he calls as they shut the heavy door.

They emerge from the Possum's lair into a parking garage. There is a booth, a row of keys. The black SUV the Possum picked them up in. The gasoline and urine smell is comforting, a thing of the daylight world. They exit quickly, looking back but not really expecting the declawed Possum to follow.

"What a coward," Neve says. "They all are, really."

They're on the street now. The city is alive with dog walkers and people heading out for breakfast. It turns out they're not far from the club.

"I fed Alex's croutons to the pigeons when he left," Rosa says. "I poured his fancy shampoo in the gutter. I don't know if I ever loved him."

"I wish I was like you," Neve says.

"What are you talking about?" Rosa stops mid-sidewalk.

"Into girls," Neve says. "We're fucked up, too, but not as entitled."

"Into girls," Rosa repeats. "Yes. That's right. I pretty much am."

Neve is still quiet. From the look of her, she's about to cry. She moves to the doorway of a pawn shop, still closed, and leans against the locked iron gate.

"I got my period," she says. "After I flushed the beard."

"Oh?" Rosa moves so she's directly in Neve's line of sight. Her odd eyes are at it again, turning her ordinary face fey and beautiful. "You're never late." Neve's period had always been moderate and regular unlike Rosa's chaotic, painful deluge.

"Right," Neve says. Her shoulders are tight. Her hands are balled into fists. "Alex came back to the dorms with me after Thanksgiving. Stayed until the term ended. We're both back home now."

"Were you... pregnant?

"That's what the test said."

Careful Neve would never let something like this happen! Alex. That asshole. This must be his fault. She opens her mouth then realizes what's next, the thing Neve may or may not admit.

"He wanted you to have it?"

Neve's head jerks, not quite a nod. "There was no way. Was always going to have an abortion," she says, "I came to ask you to come with me. I know that's beyond fucked up. I'm sorry."

"I would've done it," Rosa says.

"Yeah," Neve says. "I know."

"Why didn't you tell me about Mr. Ruel?" Rosa almost whispers the question. Neve's secrets have so much power. But then, so do Rosa's.

"I didn't want you to know," Neve says. "I didn't want anyone to know. Not ever."

They exhale in unison, letting something go. The Muni passes. Then a taxi. A tall elegant Black woman across the street walks a bright-eyed little dog.

"Should we find a diner?" Rosa says. "I'm starved."

"I have to go," Neve says. "I'm staying at my mom's. She'll be worried."

The hug starts fast, then slows way down. They hold tight and breathe together. Once, twice. Three times. They part.

"Bye," Neve says, moving to the curb to cross the street toward the BART station.

"Be safe," Rosa calls, surprised at her relief to be on her own, the way her thoughts are already on the Mexican breakfast they make at the diner across from the club.

Neve walks away in her ordinary raincoat and waterproof boots. Rosa watches until she disappears down the stairs to the train. ⓑ

'Formula No. 1 (black light)'

'Just A Sip'

Mixed Media Art: MORGAN ROSSKOPF (she/they) is a visual artist living and working in Portland, Oregon. She received her MFA in Fine Art from the University of Oregon in 2013 and her BFA in Printmaking from Sonoma State University in 2010. Rosskopf's art has appeared in numerous galleries across the world. She has received grants from the Oregon Arts Commission, and is a member of Well Well Projects Artist Collective.

A Quiet Song

Story: ALEX GREJUC (he/him)

Alex Grejuc is a Romanian-American writer and engineer who lives in Portland. He can be contacted at **alexgrejucwrites@ gmail.com.**

Paintings: JOSH GATES (he/him)

Josh Gates is a local Deaf artist captivated by fleeting conditions of weather and light. As an Oregon-raised longtime Portlander, he finds the pervasively rainy climate here beautiful and inspiring.
@joshgatesart
www.joshgatesart.com

Jordan held the flier close to his face. The words Selfie Styx were printed in blocky lettering across the top. Beneath was a sketch of two people canoeing through rapids, one paddling at the front with a guitar, another drumming in the back. On either side of the river were hundreds of wraiths, pressed against each other with selfie sticks in hand. "This is great," Jordan said as he looked at the cover charge, listed as *Free, like all the worst things in life.*

"Thanks, dude! And check it out," Eli said, rummaging through his backpack for a manila envelope. "I have a bunch more."

"Huh. And you didn't notice you forgot to write that it's at Jack's?"

"Motherfucker! I knew I was forgetting something."

After scrawling in the same address over and over with Eli's paint pen, they taped flyers on lockers, above the water fountains that still worked, outside bathrooms, and the front entrance of their high school. They stapled a couple more onto trees near the skate park. Then they walked down 82nd, taping fliers to bus stops, a motel, a Vietnamese restaurant, outside an adult video store, and even next to a strip club. "Actually, let's hold onto the last one," Eli said. "To remind us of where we started."

"Ah yes, our glorious beginnings on the mean streets," replied Jordan, gesturing towards the strip club, which resembled a tool shed in disrepair. "But you're right, though. Let's keep it." The two of them contemplated the flier and their future. Friday, September 18 at 6:00 PM. Their first real show.

They practiced as much as they could, which was not as much as they wanted. By the time they made it home from school and into Jordan's basement, there was only an hour or so before his parents came home. At that point, they had to stop or face complaints about his "raucous" drums as well as Eli's "squawking" voice and guitar. Eli's place was out of the question. He did not bring people into his home. It had always been that way, even in middle school.

Both of them did their best to convince people into going. However, beyond their few friends, nobody wanted to go.

"In Clackamas? Getting there is a mission," an acquaintance at the skatepark told Eli.

"Oh yeah. My family used to go there when it was an Applebees. Why'd you pick that place?" a guy at improv club asked.

"I might be busy," a girl in Jordan's calculus class said before he even mentioned the date.

"Yeah...doesn't really seem like our thing," his newspaper editor said. "But we might be able to fit it in the events list. Is that a conflict of interest?" he added.

The day before the show, the only person beyond their few friends who said they might attend was Mr. H, who let them screen print a few band shirts in art class. As Selfie Styx ended their final practice in Jordan's basement, he said, "Well, at least we can really say we started from the bottom."

The restaurant suffered from an identity crisis similar to the one many adolescents face—an uncertainty about what it was, a lack of commitment to any one thing. There were several TVs attached to the walls, playing college football, the news, children's cartoons, and pasta maker infomercials. In the kitchen, cooks prepared clam chowder, deep-dish pizza, and California rolls. Customers delighted in the hodgepodge and culinary diversity but the shaggy guitarist and stocky drummer getting ready to rock the house wasn't what they were expecting.

The shaggy guitarist spoke into the mic. "Hey everyone! I'm Eli and this is Jordan. His parents found me and my brothers in a soggy cardboard box on a rainy evening. They took me in, but had to drown—"

Jordan struck his cymbal and whispered, "Read the fucking room, dude."

"I mean, his parents took me in, but had to, uh, *dry* the rest of the litter. The point is, life is precious—I was only spared by chance. That's why we're gonna play our hearts out tonight!" Eli waited for a reaction from the room, but table chitchat continued. "We're called Selfie Styx. Like the river. And we're gonna start off with some covers for you." That was the deal Jordan had brokered. Only after starting with some time-tested classics could they play their own stuff. Jordan tried to keep up while his friend rushed through "Smoke on the Water," "Eye of the Tiger," and "T.N.T." Although Eli did enjoy it when the patrons joined in with a somewhat reserved "Oi! Oi! Oi! Oi!," he couldn't stop thinking about getting to play his own songs.

"Alright, now we're gonna switch over to some originals," he said as they finished the covers. "This first one is called 'Always and For Never.' Hope it makes your ears...bloom." They started playing distorted, adolescent rock. Jordan pounded the drums. Eli cooed and yelled into the mic while thrashing his strings, the dissonance spreading a wave of disapproval through the restaurant. During the second verse he sang "Fuckin" instead of "Freakin." This was the last straw for the manager, who bobbed from table to table, apologizing to customers as he approached the band. "No no no no no. Off. Off! Stop!" he yelled, waving his hands, and marching onto the stage. Jordan froze. Eli did not and kept thrashing at his guitar. A rowdy table of teenagers cheered and a man at the bar flashed horns with his hands. Then the manager yanked the power cable from the amp. "I said keep it clean! And...drowned litters? This is a family restaurant."

"Uncle Jack, just...it was a misunderstanding," Jordan said. "He didn't...everything else will be clean, I swear."

"No," he said, shaking his head. "No." He pulled out his wallet and gave them a fifty. "There's your money. You can't say I didn't hold up my end of the deal. Now go. I'm going to speak to your father about this." They packed their gear while Uncle Jack attended apologetically to his diners, offering them complimentary drinks.

"Man, what the fuck?" Jordan said to Eli when they made it outside. "I told you to keep it clean!"

"Dude, sorry," said Eli. We finally got to play our stuff and, I don't know, I just messed up. It was like muscle memory or instinct or something."

"Ohhh, muscle memory. Okay. What the fuck are you talking about? This could have been our lucky break. You just had to mess it all up."

"Oh, come on. You think a show at this lame ass place was gonna get us anywhere?"

"Nah, you're right," said Jordan, feigning agreement. "Not with lame ass lyrics like yours. Ooooh, look at me. I can cuss. I can be a misanthrope. I'm soooo edgy."

"Whatever, dude. At least I can write songs. At least I care enough to want to sing my actual lyrics. And at least I'm not trying to be a sellout."

"Well at least I can put together a band poster without fucking it up."

"Fuck off, dude," Eli said as he carried his guitar to the other end of the parking lot.

He walked back when an Isuzu dump truck pulled in. Jordan's father, Silas, stepped out of the vehicle. He barely greeted the boys. The truck bed was messy with fragments of the day's haul, so he spread a tarp on the bottom before securing the boys' instruments. Silas remained tight-lipped as he dropped Eli off at his apartment complex and on the rest of the ride home. Jordan was about to climb into the truck bed to unhook his drum kit when his father said, "Leave it there."

"What if someone steals it overnight?"

"Saves me a trip to the dump."

After an argument with his parents, Jordan shut himself in his room. He texted Eli, "I'm done with this stupid fucking band." Then he blocked Eli on his phone, unfollowed him on Instagram, and unfriended him on Snapchat.

"These respirators aren't doing shit," Jordan said to his father. They were inhaling a mixture of liquor, vomit, and death. It permeated the unit of a low-rise apartment complex.

His parents ran a junk removal company. In theory, his mom was the brains, and his dad was the brawn. In practice, the whole family of three did a little bit of everything. Sure, his mother, Meredith, handled most of the finances, the marketing, and the appointments, but she also sorted through junk to find things worth selling, and carried trash bags into the truck, a testament to one of Meredith and Silas's favorite quotes: many hands make light work. And yes, his father did much of the heavy lifting, but he also solicited customers-to-be in hardware stores and even on vacations, writing names in blocky print with his carpenter's pencil on whichever receipt he had folded in his pockets. He attributed his success in these interactions to his yearly study of Dale Carnegie's oeuvre—just about the only literature he had read in the last two decades.

From an early age, Jordan was involved in the family enterprise. Apart from lifting junk, he was expected to list finds on Craigslist,

update the website, and figure out everything else that involved technology. What he hated most was that his parents regularly gave him business cards, which he never passed out.

"Well, the faster we work, the sooner we can go," Silas said. "But since you're here, why don't you take it in? This guy was an alcoholic. He tried to kill himself using a belt around his neck." There was still dried blood on the floor next to a plastic half-gallon of vodka, and a hole in the ceiling.

"This sure is some good father-son bonding," Jordan said as he wandered around the apartment. It was littered with empty liquor bottles and cans of beer. Clothes crusted with urine and vomit were scattered around the apartment. Everything was clogged in the bathroom; the scummy tub was a swamp. The few items in the fridge were expired.

"How about you shut it and help me with this couch," commanded Silas. "You need money for college."

As Jordan walked over he said, "No, you *want* me to need money for college."

"Did you know that this guy was a musician? This is the path you want to choose?" Silas asked. Jordan did not have a sarcastic reply—but felt a morsel of reckoning that he would not share with his father. He squatted, bent at the knees, and counted aloud 1-2-3-LIFT, just as his father had trained. They carried the couch out of the house, into the back of the Isuzu, and continued back and forth with the rest of the furniture and trash. While Jordan was removing drawers from a desk, he found the alcoholic's tax returns and résumé. The guy was an accountant.

"I swear to God. *One* cup of wine. *One*. Literally, it was the dumbest thing ever!" said the girl sitting behind Eli.

"Fuck. At least I was shitfaced," a guy replied.

It was Saturday, Eli and twenty other teenagers from across the school district were in a classroom, waiting for the Alcohol IQ® pre-assessment. Then they would participate in a four-hour course about the dangers of underage drinking, followed by a post-assessment.

At 8:00am, a middle-aged instructor wearing an Alcohol IQ® polo shirt entered the classroom. As the instructor was handing out worksheets, another student slinked in late. It was Jordan.

After the assessment, Eli moved to a desk beside Jordan. "So, how have you been?" he asked. Jordan ignored him. "Whatever, dude," replied Eli. Their interactions continued in this fashion. When materials were passed around the class, Jordan skipped Eli. When the students had to form groups with others around them, Jordan moved to the other side of the room. When the instructor asked for examples of bad influences, Jordan told a passive-aggressive story about his friend *Levi*.

The response could have left Eli despondent, but it was during a break when he struck upon a plan that charged him with enthusiasm. He was getting a drink from a water fountain when he overheard, "Recognize you...parties I've been to...fun crowd."

Fun crowd. The two words were tectonic. The Alcohol IQ® class

'Avenue of Roses'

collected all the cool, party kids from across the school district. His classmates knew how to get booze and how to have a good time with it. Plus, it wasn't *just* going to be a party. He would invite Jordan, they'd play a show, wow the crowd, and then the band would be back together.

Eli began networking at once. He started conversations at urinals, water fountain lines, and during breakout sessions, all in the name of the party-to-be. Eli had spread the word to all twenty students, the reception universally positive, except for Jordan's. "No," he said when Eli asked if he would play just one show.

"Come on, man. I lost us a gig, I got us a gig. The math checks out," Eli reasoned.

"I'm done, dude. I'm done playing music." The two of them fell silent. Although Jordan had thought about quitting music, he never said it out loud.

"Shit, man. Is it 'cause of your dad? You need me to—"

"Look. I don't wanna talk about it."

Once they had taken their post-assessments and finished the class, Jordan was the first out of the building.

A month passed before they said another word to each other. Eli's mom read a book about decluttering and decided the house was overrun with junk.

"No. No fuckin' way," Eli told her while crumpling a frozen pizza box.

"Eli! Quit bein' a baby," she said before lifting the last slice. "They would give us a good deal."

"I told you, me and Jordan don't talk anymore."

"Fine. Then I'll just look them up myself."

"No way," Jordan said as he scooped broccoli into his plate.

"Oh, come on. Get over it. I need your help," Silas replied.

And so, Jordan found himself in Eli's apartment. Mix-matched furniture crowded the living room, bookcases and shelves were overflowing.

"Eli! Get out of your room! The gentlemen need your help!" his mom yelled.

Without opening his door, Eli replied, "No they don't."

She opened the bedroom door and raised her voice. "Stop bein' a pain in the ass. Say hi to your friend. Hug it out and make up. And then help them get this shit out of the fuckin' house! I'm having a do-over. Don't kill my momentum."

Eli shuffled out of his room while muttering, "You'll just find some new shit to replace the old shit." He sidled through a hallway congested with sagging boxes and avoided eye contact with Jordan while helping him lift an overfilled crate. They hefted it on a winding path around the peeling furniture and into the truck bed. "So, you find anyone else to play with?" Jordan asked.

"Nah. I swear, everyone's so flakey."

Silas and the boys hauled junk while Eli's mom found new things to part ways with. Each item she got rid of—including an exercise bike, a cat tree, a kiddie pool and half her infomercial appliances—gave her a rush. She went in and out of rooms announcing, "But wait, there's more!"

Jordan was on his way out when Eli asked, "You sure you don't wanna play? Not even one last show? I really planned this one out."

"Nah man, good luck though."

"Alright, see ya around, I guess."

"See ya," Jordan said. He got inside the truck.

"So? You see how those people live?" Silas said.

"As if your business doesn't depend on them," Jordan replied.

The acrid tendrils of fertilizer suffocated the scent of lavender. Eli and his three friends could smell it. They were walking along a flower-lined path, crunching gravel underneath their feet. "Dude. It smells like shit," one friend said.

"Only on every other breath," Eli replied. He was lugging a guitar case. The party planning committee had chosen this spot via group chat: Melanie's parents' house. It was on a small, private vineyard in Lake Oswego. The music got louder as they approached until they reached the entrance, and it was all they could hear. Eli inspected the knocker, an iron cluster of grapes, and opened the door.

The loud music was a false promise. It was barely a party. Just Migos vibrating the family portraits on the walls and random groups of teenagers too awkward to venture away from their friends. Two of them were engaged in a slow game of beer pong on the back porch, visible through all the unpeopled space of the house. Most of the attendees were on their phones. The dancing, the laughter, the shotgunning, and the making out was not going as effortlessly as they had imagined.

"I thought you said it was gonna be epic," Eli's friend said.

"I told you the Lake Oswego kids would let us down," another friend reminded him.

"I bet half of them are studying for the SAT or practicing their clarinet or whatever," the third one said.

"Jesus, will you guys chill? People will show up eventually," replied Eli. Although he put on an air of confidence, he was full of self-doubt. He hyped up his house show and dragged his friends to the west side to attend it. Fortunately, they had a solution in a backpack: a thirty rack. Eli and his friends cracked open cans of Rainier. The beer in Eli's hand emboldened him to wander away from his friends. After stowing his guitar, he approached a guy in a bucket hat from the Alcohol IQ® class. "Hey, man," he said.

"What's up!"

"Oh, you know, just chillin'."

"Hell yeah. What's your name again?"

"Eli."

"Right. I'm Cody," he said as he put his fist out for a bump. Eli obliged. Then they avoided eye contact while straining for a topic of conversation.

"So uhh, this is a pretty bougie house, huh?" Eli said.

"Oh yeah. Nicest one off the lake." After a few seconds of silence, Cody asked, "You go to Riverdale, right?"

"Nah, Madison. And you're at Lake Oswego?"

"Yeah."

"Cool, cool." They paused again. "I'm playing tonight."

"What?"

"I'm playing in the show."

"Oh. What band?"

"Well, the other guy couldn't make it, so it's just me, actually. But we're called Selfie Styx. Like the river."

"There's a river called Selfie Sticks?"

"Nah, like from Greek mythology, ya know? The River Styx. With an X."

"Oh, yeah, right. I think I know which ones you're talking about," Cody said before looking past Eli.

"Well, I'll catch ya later," Eli said.

He tried a few more conversations before giving up and retreating to the living room couch where his friends sat. The front door opened every few minutes and soon enough, conversation flowed as people rubbed shoulders, spilled beer, noticed each others' cool t-shirts, and realized they had the same favorite songs.

"Shit, dude. This *is* going to be epic," one of Eli's friends said. Perhaps it was, but Eli could not get over the thought that his best friend was not coming, and that Selfie Styx was now a solo act. It stung when the first band started playing near the unlit fireplace. Their sound was preppy and eclectic rock that included a keyboardist. And it was organized. The frontwoman sang lyrics that were probably clever and definitely catchy. The growing crowd was dancing. Eli felt out of his depth.

Then he felt a playful tap on his shoulder. He turned to see Melanie, the host, who was gripping a box of wine. "Hey! Thanks for putting this together!" she said.

"Thanks for letting us use your place!"

"So, are you ready?"

"I don't know. These guys are pretty good. Looks like I'm gonna continue my lifelong habit of disappointing people."

Melanie laughed. She held out the wine. "Well, if you need some liquid courage…."

"What the hell, sure," Eli said before taking a swig. They passed the wine back and forth as they talked. She was flirting, although he would not realize that until many days later, when it would jolt him awake right before sleep.

When the preppy band finished their set, it was his turn to play. As he dawdled towards the makeshift stage, the energy of the party decreased. He felt like hundreds of eyes were on him as he fumbled with the amp, his guitar, the instrument cable, and the mic.

What everyone saw was a swaying, gangly, and lackadaisical teenager. But the truth was that Eli was giving one hundred percent to simultaneously stand, keep track of his guitar, and not burp. It was not enough. "Hey everyone. I'm…" he rotated away from the mic to belch, though it was still somewhat amplified. Some people laughed, others groaned, and just about everyone paid attention, including Melanie. "Sorry about that. I'm Eli. This is my band. Well, half my band. The other guy is, um, on sabbatical. Anyways, uhhh, we're called Selfie Styx. This…" Someone shouted something from the crowd that he couldn't quite catch. Eli looked up.

The voice shouted again. "Like the river?" It was Jordan.

"Yeah. Selfie Styx," said Eli. "Like the fuckin' river!"

The crowd made space for Jordan to walk towards the fireplace.

"You showed up! Was this your plan the whole time?" Eli asked.

"Nah, dude. I just came here to get drunk. But then you cringed me sober." Jordan requested permission to use the drums, and Melanie blasted music on the house speakers. She found Eli an energy drink and sent him to the bathroom to splash water on his face and gather himself.

After adjusting the kit, Jordan approached the mic. "Hey everyone," he said motioning to Melanie to turn down the Post Malone. "I'm not supposed to be here. I quit the band a couple of months ago because Eli is kind of a dumbass, as you can see." The crowd chuckled. "But I guess he's also my best friend."

"Awwww," the crowd swooned.

Eli returned, slung on his guitar, and said, into the mic, "I know that you really need some live music after all this waiting. Once again, I'm Eli, this is Jordan and we're called Selfie Styx."

"Like the river!" a few people shouted.

"Fuck yeah!" Eli said. "This is our latest song, 'Expletive Censored!'" It was "Always and For Never," sung with new lyrics. They played an unforgettable set. The music of a band that hadn't figured out their sound—a distorted and fast indie rock orgy of grunge, blues, psychedelia, and punk. Revealing pits stained with sweat, Jordan peppered, crashed, pounded, and punched the borrowed kit. It ranged from war drum to speed bag. Eli shredded, whined, and yowled. He experimented with his pedalboard. He spewed lyrics and saliva. He shut his eyes and tuned into ethereal frequencies. It was the music of fireworks and blenders; cinnamon, ginger, chili powder, and vinegar; the sound of a coarse and jagged cliffside scratching a rock and roll record.

It was all over the place. Fresh and honest, but lacking clarity and practice. Jordan was rusty. He hadn't played in a while. He muttered, "Shit" several times throughout the show. And Eli was still quite drunk. Their music suffered from too much inspiration and inebriation. Fortunately, the crowd was quite drunk too— and not especially discerning in their response. It was late. They had live music to listen to—they were going to dance, shout, and have a good time regardless. They sweated, contorted, and jumped to the beat of Jordan's drum and the rhythm of Eli's guitar until somebody yelled, "He's not moving! Call 9-1-1!" from the kitchen.

Not long after, an ambulance, a fire truck, and the police showed up to save Cody, who had tried to keep up with his friends. The EMTs stretchered him out and the police broke the party up.

Perhaps it was the sheer number of attendees (*What are you gonna do? Bust us all?*), the zip code, or a mix of the two, but the cops only issued one citation and that was for poor Melanie (*I swear to God. I threw one party. One. Literally, it was the dumbest thing ever!*). The notification of parents and the ride home, of course, was its own punishment.

Parents practically abducted teenagers until the crowd shrank to perhaps only a dozen partygoers. Eli had turned down the last remaining seat in a car with his other friends. He had just gotten through to Jordan, and he was not going to let him suffer alone. So, he sat beside him on the curb. They knew Silas would not be happy. They knew it while considering making the call, as they waited for him to answer, while he barked through the phone so loud that Jordan had to pull it away from his ear.

When Silas arrived, Eli and Jordan climbed into the truck, buckled their seatbelts, and prepared for the dressing down. But Silas started with disconcerting calmness. "Haven't we been here before? What is it with the two of you?"

No one answered, and they drove three blocks in silence. Then Silas erupted. "What's the excuse, Jordan? Don't you have parents that love you? Don't we feed you and put a roof over your head? Don't you know how lucky you are? Are you so ungrateful that you have to run around pretending to be some troubled youth? Huh? Let me guess. Life just isn't *fun* enough for you. Is that what they teach you these days? Have fun. You think your mom and I want to work every day?" All Eli could do was look out the window and pretend he wasn't there until Silas yanked him into the tempest, too, "And you. You and your fucking guitar! This is the last ride you ever get from me. I don't know why I don't

just leave you on the side of the road."

Silas took a breath and was about to continue his brimstone, but Jordan raised his voice louder than his father's. "Why the hell should we listen to you?"

"Oh, so you know everything! At the age of eighteen you've got it *all* figured out!"

"That's fucking bullshit! And what is it with the mind games? Why can't you just express your adult thoughts to your adult son in an adult way?"

"In an adult w—"

"You tell me stories about the crazy shit you and your friends were up to back in the day. Getting into fights, sneaking into bars, the time you crashed your motorcycle, and on, and on, and on. What the hell do you expect me to learn from that? You want me to emulate only the responsible half of you? You get to be imperfect while I have to be perfect? And did I do anything truly idiotic? I called you for a ride."

This last explosion produced three great quiets. Quiets that harmonized in a song of ephemeral understanding as their headlights illuminated the winding wooded roads of southwest Portland. Their song rang out while they crossed the Sellwood Bridge and the murky waters of the Willamette that flowed underneath it. It rested as they passed the amusements of Oaks Park, swirled with the cool air that rushed into the car, and resonated as they arrived at Eli's apartment complex.

"I'm gonna spend the night at Eli's," Jordan said, and the two exited the truck.

"Alright," said Silas before driving away.

Jordan tried to sleep on the floor of Eli's room that night, but the lingering adrenaline kept him up for much of it. He reflected on the evening and marveled at the music they made. He knew it was not perfect. But memory has a way of smoothing the finer details, of erasing the lack of greatness to reveal the abundance of goodness. Like waves splashing onto rocks, Jordan would come back to the evening over and over. This boulder of a memory, after so much weathering, would reduce to grains of sand in between the crevices of newer and larger rocks, seemingly insignificant but essential. ⓑ

A Progressive Tarot Reading for the City of Portland

Foreword & Curation: COLEMAN STEVENSON (she/her)

Coleman Stevenson is the author of three collections of poems (*Light Sleeper, Breakfast*, and *The Accidental Rarefication of Pattern #5609*), several books about the Tarot including *The Dark Exact Tarot Guide* and a series of cartomantic spread collections. Her writing has appeared in a variety of literary journals, anthologies, and websites. In addition to her work as a designer of tarot and oracle decks through her company The Dark Exact, her fine art work, exhibited in galleries around the US, focuses on the intersections between image and text.
colemanstevenson.com

Reading: STEPHANIE ADAMS-SANTOS (she/they)

Stephanie Adams-Santos is a Guatemalan-American writer whose work spans poetry, prose, and screenwriting, with a penchant for the queer and fantastical. She is the author of *Dream of Xibalba* (forthcoming, winner of the Orison Prize in Poetry), *Swarm Queen's Crown* (finalist for the Lambda Literary Awards), *Total Memory*, and *The Sundering* (selected for a New York Chapbook Fellowship by Poetry Society of America). Stephanie was a story editor on the CW television anthology series *Two Sentence Horror Stories* (now on Netflix), is a writer on an upcoming 20th Century/Disney+ live action fantasy series, and is developing an original fantasy pilot as part of the 2022 Ojala Ignition Fellowship.
obscurobeach.com
@Tarot_Obscuro

Reading: GIVEN Q. DAVIS (he/they)

Given Q. Davis is a multidisciplinary artist, tarot reader, and nonprofit consultant in Portland, Oregon, navigating the world in a magical queer, Black, nonbinary, transmasculine body. He has been a Reiki Master and Portland resident for 10 years.
bloomingfirehealing.com
@bloomingfirepdx
@givenqdaviswrites

Reading: ERIK L. ARNESON (he/him)

Erik L. Arneson is a practicing magician who got his first Tarot deck in the late 1980s and has worked with the cards in some capacity ever since. With decades of experience in Western esotericism, he has lectured at conferences, and taught classes about Ceremonial Magic, Tarot, and the Art of Memory. Erik is the host of the Arnemancy Podcast.
arnemancy.com
@arnemancy.

Reading: MICHELLE RUIZ KEIL (she/her)

Bio on page 47.

The Infloresence deck was illustrated by MICHAEL ARMENIA. Find more of his work at **@doctusbalatro** and **michaelarmenia.com**.

What is next for this city? Especially as spaces and people we've loved for decades disappear and new citizens and businesses take their places, what values will our expanding city hold and how will we express them? Who will guide this process, and what place does each of us have in the future of Portland?

I called on the Tarot and several local reader friends to collaboratively address these questions—folks I've worked with over my decades in Portland at different times and in various capacities, trusted interpreters of the cards, each with their own deep connections to this place.

We were tasked with using the Tarot to examine the current state of affairs in Portland and explore where we might be headed collectively, hopefully finding a way to interpret with optimism whatever cards came up. Creative individuals and networks are vital to the functioning of any healthy city, so we chose to focus the reading on how Portland's artists, writers, makers, and doers might usher us all through this period of uncertainty in the city's identity.

Each reader focused on a specific question within this larger theme and pulled a card or two. We shared our cards with each other to establish a sense of the reading as a whole, and certain themes were clearly present.

The desire for collaboration I felt with this assignment is echoed in the cards themselves.

There is also a call for greater understanding and compassion, for paying closer attention to the lives of others, and a push to act once perspectives have shifted. We hope the following questions, cards, and interpretations will resonate with your lives here in Portland, among family, friends, neighbors, and strangers. And most of all, we hope that within these words and images, you'll find a spark motivating you to be part of positive change, or uncover something that shows you your personal path forward into the new life of our shared city.

For this reading, we used a common deck, the Inflorescence Tarot, which I made in collaboration with PNW artist Michael Armenia. The art for this deck developed gradually over two years, via digital transmission during the pandemic. The depiction of the Tarot characters in this deck is abstract, presenting the essences and moods of the cards through color and pattern in what we think of as "inflorescences," the flowering of each card's spirit. This encouraged our cohort of readers to have a more intuitive, contemplative experience with the cards rather than immediately defaulting to preconceived notions about them, influenced by more archetypal imagery. This introspective process echoes the sentiments encouraging us all to seek new perspectives, act collaboratively, and continue tending the garden that is the Rose City and all our lives within it.

This reading is meant to energize and inspire revitalization at a key crossroads in Portland's history.

Question: What kind of paradigm shift is needed in Portland at present, and how can our creative community instigate and inspire positive change in our city?

The Tower leapt from the deck to address the first half of this question. The Tower aptly calls out to us in our moment of mass destabilization. Portlanders have collectively been navigating the ongoing pandemic, bracing for the unknowns of another pivotal wake-up call to actively support Black lives, trans lives, reproductive rights, and the rights of those who are currently unhoused. The list goes on and on. The miasma is thick. However, this card offers us the opportunity to clear the clouds and see ourselves more accurately than ever before. The cracks in the proverbial structure have run too far and deep to continue bearing the weight of what has been. Our city has been shaken in order to break us open to the truth of the times. And it's a little different from "the big one" we've been bracing for.

To be bold, we could reframe this moment as a fortuitous disaster.

As the fog of false belief in an idealized Portland disperses, for many, there remains a desire to hold our communities closer than ever. This is a period of re-grounding, not as the same individuals and communities we've been, but as the city we dream ourselves to be. Like the negative space in the Tower card, we have been given a blank page. It is our work to reveal the intricate latticework that holds us together. Sacred geometry runs beneath, within, and through the grey. There is no "I" in Portland. We must ask ourselves: To what people, places, things, and ideas are we already connected and committed? To which communities do they belong? We are being called to notice the ways that ripples in one circle of Portland intimately impact the next. Perhaps we were not present to be a part of constructing what the city has been, but our presence can support what our city becomes.

The 7 of Wands lights the way for Portland's creative community to ignite change. The Wands suit is associated with the element of fire, and illuminates our relationship to power, desire, and drive. So, dear creatives, in order to be of service to the greater web, we are being asked to rise to the occasion and to identify those ways in which we feel grounded, motivated, and prepared to take leadership roles within our respective disciplines. This is not a suggestion to pursue clout or positions for the sake of a title. It is about the way we are able to dream up new possibilities and bring them into being. Ideally, those bright visions will resonate with others. With hope, we can join forces with those who can meet us in broadening narratives and creating change within oppressive systems.

It is difficult for the eye to settle when looking at the 7 of Wands. Each circle draws attention, and the image almost seems to pulse. Heads up! This particular energy has the potential to create a contentious venture out of the highest of intentions. If we do find ourselves or others quoting from Highlander—"In the end, there can only be one"—then it's time to reconsider our motives. Focus. Do a bit of soul searching to locate the wick of our "why" to help our grand plans stay on course. Re-center what came to mind with the Tower and the centrifugal force of intention. Utilize the fire of any frustration to propel the work forward.

If experiencing tense collaborations, continued conflict without interruption only ensures the elongation of muddling through already unsure times. When in doubt, we would do well to seek outside facilitators and mediators early to navigate tense conversations and provide a stabilizing force. The traditional image of the 7 of Wands depicts a central figure fending off multiple external forces. That is all of us right now. We will hold our ground where we need to, but rather than picking fights or responding to hostility with more of the same, we might consider approaching with curiosity. We can either inflict pain for pain or lean into our shared humanity. A willingness to share differing perspectives and personal experiences within the context of what we love and hold close to our hearts might just remind us that, although variable in the details, the shape of many of our lives is ultimately similar. We must advocate for our truth and invest presence and energy in the people, places, things, and ideas that feed our creative power and allow it to fuel the way forward. Be the Laurelhurst Joan of Arc. Stand for something and work to create that change courageously. Victoriously.

Balancing both our individual and collective efforts may not be easy, but it's worth it.

To further connect with the energies represented in these cards, we must ask: What does it mean to be a leader? Why do that? What support is or can be reciprocal? How are you inviting cross-pollination? What is worth fighting for? What creations are most resonant with your internal fire? What ticks you off enough to create change?

Reader: Given Q. Davis

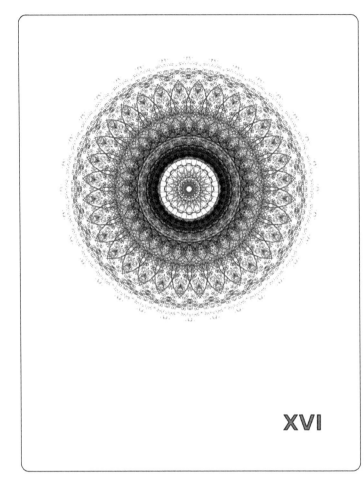

XVI

The Tower
Listening recommendation:
"Burn It Blue" by Caetano Veloso
& Lila Downs

7 of Wands
Listening recommendation:
"Tear Me Down" by Steven Trask from Hedwig &
the Angry Inch

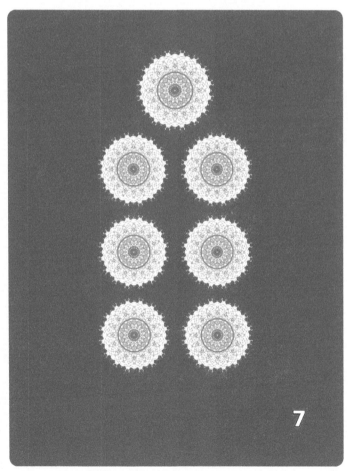

7

Question: How do we foster harmony and communication among disparate realms of the city that may have very different needs and goals?

A vital return to the ecological/cosmological imagination is in order. From this, courage and inspiration will propel us individually and collectively toward new visions and modes of community that are more just and tender and generous and caring.

Imagine yourself for a moment as a red-tailed hawk crossing over the Rose City. See the many arches over which lines of traffic move to and fro like ants, just another creature of this complex ecosystem. Portland is stitched together by bridges. *St. Johns, Ross Island, Steel, Hawthorne...* But consider how the river running through it is a living bridge from mountain to sea. The forest is a bridge, the sky a bridge. Perspective, too, is a bridge. Consciousness, a bridge, our very thoughts made from the bridges of synapse.

> *There is a place always beneath*
> > *and above this place*
> > > *There is a bridge always extending*
> > > > *into places I do not yet know*

This city will always be more than we know it to be. It is shaped by forces ancient and new, human and non-human, home for countless species other than our own. Here be crows, porcupines, coyotes, owls, bobcats, beavers. We all know the daddy-longlegs lurking in the cellar. The mouse, the rat, the skunk. This place is a home even for those we'd rather not consider.

> *You are mirrored*
> > *in all that you love*
> > > *You are mirrored*
> > > > *in all that you revile*

Consider how there are things we don't want to consider out of fear, out of inconvenience. And for lack of consideration, there are things that have disappeared — species, habitats, people, and beings that we've shuttered out of belonging by a simple lack of courage and connection.

> *A bridge can collapse upon itself*

When we shorten certain bridges out of carelessness, we blunt the edges of our own being. As we dream up our own realities, we ought to have the courage and generosity of spirit to include the imagining of other lives, other bodies, other species, other experiences. Consider that with which we communicate as that with which we foster a relationship. With whom do we commune? Our human community, our non-human community; the land itself; the elements. Consider the oxygen in our blood, made from the trees that populate the periphery of our gazes like mute statues. To be without oxygen for a matter of minutes can mean brain damage, or death — our entire world of dreams and thoughts and desires, gone. Trees, then, ought to be among our closest and most cherished companions. Yet these mysterious Others can become quickly invisible and excluded from our primal understanding of community or selfhood, though they are vital to all those things. A tree in a parking lot is scarcely valued or paid any mind, as when we walk by an unhoused person without consideration of their reality, their vital presence, the many bridges that connect our lives. How might we expand our notions of community and communication with such Others in mind? How might we seek to make room for greater awareness of the vast living networks we are each a vital part of? This kind of individual visioning strengthens the harmony of the collective Whole.

> *Boundlessly I love*
> > *from the fount of the spirit*
> > > *Boundless the spirit*
> > > > *from the forge of the sun*

The Empress

III

VIII

Strength

Consider Strength as an expansion of the self, a robust and eager tenderness in action. The endless generative life-force is most potent and accessible when we are open to surprise, open to shifts and openings within the self, open to seeing Others in new ways, open to radical empathy and imagination. How do we work this muscle within ourselves?

Imagination is the first act of magic

Begin in the body
where all things are dismantled and re-shaped.

Begin in the body
where the world meets us,

where sea and star pass through on their migrations

As the Empress reminds us, our bodies are sites of migration and conversation. There is no vacuum. Everything touches. *Being* is a bridge. We are, in fact, made of other lives. We are palimpsests, erasures, cross-written spells. "All lifeforms are in fact processes not things"*. Life is continual transformation and exchange. We are woven of Otherness, made of strange materials and alchemies. We are bridged with mystery, "edged with mist"**, which extends us always toward the Other. The imagination begins in the body. At the crux of all our creative and transformative powers is our innate creaturely curiosity, with all its startling capacity for connection.

I reach beyond myself
because I know that I begin and end there

I find my own heart
here, there

We have vast capacity for love in all that we communicate. To communicate is to commune. To commune is to share an intimacy of place, of spirit, of belonging. Communication is a bridge.

A woman reaching into the Lion's mouth —

Green, the bridges between us!

You yourself are a living bridge, making and unmaking yourself each moment of existence. What visions compel you? Toward what do you reach? What beauty are you capable of imagining in yourself, in others, in this City?

We do not yet know
the shape of things to come —

The bridge is alive.
It breathes, it sloughs its skin —

It has not finished weaving the shape,
the shimmering arc of its animal form.

It is being made, even now,
by you who is reading these words.

Reader: Stephanie Adams-Santos

* —*Merlin Sheldrake* ** —*Virginia Woolf*

Question: If we reinvest fully in our city, what will we collectively be able to achieve? What story will we be able to tell next?

Looking at the tarot in terms of cycles of four, fives represent new beginnings—both a reset and a challenge. Five in the suit of Wands wants to talk about justice, perseverance, and the activation of true will through adversity. The color red in this gorgeous card summons fire & blood as life force rather than symbols of destruction. The energy and movement in the figures point to how we might remain present and constructive in an environment of strife.

Here in Portland, we sometimes cling to a remembered city, innocent, a little awkward—in some ways years behind its glamorous siblings to the north and south. But inequality in Portland has been a feature from the very beginning of the white settler theft and colonization of this land. In 1859, when Oregon became a state, it was founded as a "white utopia" where Black people were forbidden to live—the only state in the country to do so. Income inequality and housing instability are consequences of Portland's recent glow-up. Every day I see the Five of Wands as I go about my business—the chic new apartment buildings, high-end boutiques and outposts of luxury brands a surreal backdrop to camps of unhoused Portlanders.

Strife. Conflict. Burning. No escape.

The Five of Wands asks us to use our ember-bright willpower to tolerate this time of contradiction, to keep the fire burning, the conversation moving. We cannot and will not all agree. But we can be in dialogue with systems of power, holding strong, staying present, until something softens, opens, releases, renews. In the face of so much dire need, telling a new story will require steadfastness and sacrifice from all of us, as well as looking to new models and past innovations to help us find a way forward.

In the meantime, I want to dream with you.

Let's start at the heart and dream of a forest that encircles a city with a river for a spine. Let's imagine a night with a bright round moon that calls every living thing in the city to earth, a golden lullaby, irresistible. We lie down, bodies to ground. We sleep.

The rising tides, the warming planet, a warning chorus of whale song, the trees themselves—something has called the deep consciousness of the mycelia in our city forest and tree-lined streets to notice us. Perhaps we exert a pressure they feel as we lie all together on the skin of the earth. Aware, their filaments snake through our sleeping minds, leaving something new behind.

We wake and rise. We don't speak of it but whenever we meet the eyes of another animal—and we are all animals here—there is knowing passed back and forth. We know they know. They know we do. They/We. All of us. We find a way to live simply and well. The change webs out to other places, to the world.

It's a dream. My dream. What is yours? Let's make a cauldron of them. It will bubble and hiss, swirling with our intentions. It will fuel the fire that leads us out to protest in the streets, to organize, make our art and write our stories, care for one another, and continue to fight for reproductive rights, for Black lives, for food, housing, and healthcare for all.

We will keep the fire going. We will survive to tell a new story. New leaders will emerge. Indigenous science will unfurl and root in places that once scorned the oldest ways of knowing. We will learn from our youth and listen to our elders. We will be radical in our ability to hold two ideas at once. Three ideas. More! A fractal consciousness, aware that division is illusion and that no one thrives when one of us suffers.

Reader: Michelle Ruiz Keil

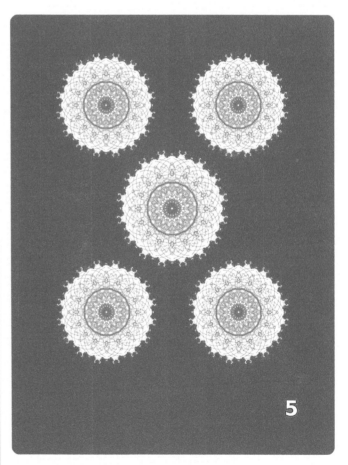

5 of Wands

Question: What do we need to do first? How do we prioritize our efforts in a way that feels harmonious?

A splash of yellow brings a surprising change in both color and feeling to this reading, but this card, the Two of Swords, isn't going to be a very easy one. The roundels on this card are spiny and spiked, even down to their nuclei, and once they get a hold of us, they won't be letting go. The Two of Swords is impossible to evade once you encounter it. Swords are the suit of elemental Air, and as such, they represent the intellectual world. This world is logical, procedural, and even inevitable. It rarely makes much room for feelings and emotional health—the Swords will tell you the harsh truth and completely ignore your hopes and dreams. This is a valuable service they do for us, even if we may not like it. It is easy to get caught up in the romantic dream of Portland as a vibrant city full of creativity, freedom, love, and opportunity. We want to love Stumptown without thinking about its dark side. Well, the Two of Swords is here to make sure, first and foremost, that we keep our perspective.

The Two is like a cell that has just finished its first division. It can now look at itself and reflect, but in doing so, might realize that the path forward isn't immediately clear or predictable. Reflection shows us that there is a long, deep history in our city that isn't quite as easy and wonderful as we'd like it to be. At the same time, Two is an unstable number in Tarot. It wants to become Three. It wants to continue the path of creation and growth, and indeed we cannot stop growth. Reflection cannot help but enable growth, which is good, because we will need that reflection to prepare for our next card.

The Ten of Pentacles can be a very happy, content card. However, we want it to help us answer the question, "How do we prioritize our efforts in a way that feels harmonious?" The roundels on this card bring to mind an arrangement of dwellings in a settlement—nine smaller camps around a larger, stronger one in the middle. This arrangement speaks of coordination and some type of harmony, but how can we get there? Pentacles are the suit of elemental Earth, and that element is the most physical, practical, and material of all the suits in Tarot. Earth can deal with wealth, location, and material goods. It is worldly to the extreme, symbolizing all the places where plans are actually brought to action, where results can be seen, and where resources are made and allocated.

Tens in the Minor Arcana (both the Two of Swords and Ten of Pentacles are part of the 56-card Minor Arcana) can point toward complete pictures, finished solutions, and even a dénouement. We should look at this card as a vision of where to go, and not necessarily the current state of things. And for this, I really enjoy the metaphor of the camps working together, well organized and cooperative. However, "cooperation" seems like both an obvious and useless answer to our question. Of course cooperation is necessary; this tells us nothing. The camps, however, could represent all manner of different groups: economic and social classes, neighborhoods, religions, ethnicities, and so forth. Their harmonious layout in this card tells me that the way we work towards prioritizing efforts and operating in harmony is to do what we can to both understand and interact with these other camps. Try to learn how other Portlanders think. Keep your ears open, that you may hear what people who are not in your camp are saying.

One hurdle that constantly plagues our city is NIMBYism—those who acknowledge that change needs to happen but are unwilling to let it happen in their backyard. However, the harmony of the dwellings in this settlement means that each has to be willing to accept and share in the changes that are ahead. We need to understand what those changes mean not just for our own camp, but also for the camps we need to work with.

Reader: Erik L. Arneson

2 of Swords

2

10 of Pentacles

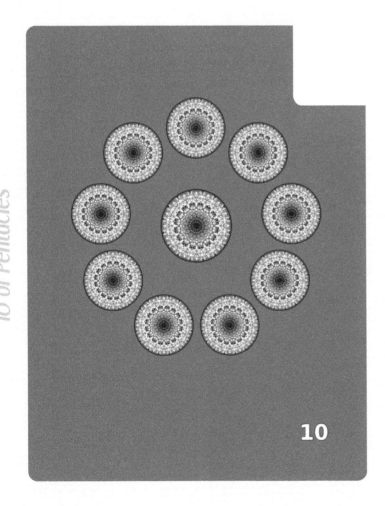

10

Ace of Wands

Question: What is each individual's role in this city's future? (*Each reader of this article is invited to think about how this card might apply to them personally.*)

To conclude the reading, I asked one final question, keeping in mind the previous cards and all the information they presented. The Ace of Wands is a powerful answer. It is a blunt reminder that ideas are wonderful—many wonderful ventures begin there, of course—but if we stay in the realm of ideas, no actual change occurs. The fire of the suit of Wands is connected to both internal spiritual energy and the energy of external action. This Ace is the concentrated power of a fresh start: a new project, a new approach, a jolt of inspiration, a new sense of our own creative potential.

Think about the current season, all the bulbs that have been planted underground, storing up energy again throughout the winter. According to this card, you are one of these bulbs, recharging now. Spring is coming for you, too. The bloom you have within awaits. Maybe some strange alchemy is even occurring beneath the soil...maybe the flower that opens in spring is not the same one you've grown before, but something new, something surprising. Maybe you will be more than you thought you could be in this approaching season. This node of potential, of bound-up energy that wants desperately to bloom, applies to work within the self – being the person you are capable of being – but also to external goals and ways you can participate in your community. Feel that concentration of power within and find the best direction to point your efforts. Focus on whatever thrills you enough that you'll sustain that enthusiasm through a whole new cycle of growth.

Looking at this card is like looking into the throat of that flower as it's blooming. The center from which everything emerges is dense and dark. As the eye moves outward, the design expands—the unfolding of a new self. The solid orange line encountered next is an important boundary. It's good to have boundaries; they protect you and can foster good communication. But this is also where you must make a decision. Do you stay within the confines of your own life, or do you choose to unfold further? If you do extend beyond the wall of the self and engage with others, look at what is possible... New color emerges, and even finer, more beautiful patterns and connections entwine in the green vining filagree. The furthest edge of the image is bordered with what appear to be hooks ready to join with others to form countless new patterns, making something greater than you ever thought possible—all through generative connection.

If you're feeling a heaviness from The Tower or tension from the Seven of Wands, the first cards in this reading, let this Ace of Wands be a relief to you. This is the opportunity to start again with a clearer sense of what matters to you most. As Given so eloquently states, "As the fog of false belief in an idealized Portland disperses, for many, there remains a desire to hold our communities closer than ever." Feeling like things just won't grow for you after your Tower experience? Sometimes you need to amend the soil. Seek out new inspiration to fertilize yours. Plenty of wondrous things remain in this city, and new grassroots offerings emerge on what seems like a daily basis. Spend some time in a neighborhood other than your own. Eat the food, encounter the art, engage with the people who are engaged.

If you have felt disconnected from others around you, the Strength and Empress cards show you how you are never really alone and urge you to loosen your boundaries in healthy ways. "The endless generative life-force is most potent and accessible when we are open to surprise, open to shifts and openings within the self, open to seeing Others in new ways, open to radical empathy and imagination," Stephanie gently encourages. It's true – you are not a lone flower in the middle of an endless field. You are emerging in the midst of many flowers, each with its own beautiful arrangement of petals. Appreciate the ways others are blooming and all their unique traits. It's not a competition – it's a garden, which we see echoed in the Five of Wands. With that card, Michelle calls up images of a great mycelial network of which we are all a part, in which we share energy and receive new ideas: "Aware, their filaments snake through our sleeping minds, leaving something new behind." She reminds us that it is never too late to tell a new story. Each season renews that chance, and even conflict, says the Five of Wands, is part of progress. Conflict is an opportunity to rewrite the narrative into one of collaboration and sustainable compromise.

Lastly, the Two of Swords wants us to stop and reflect as the first action for this change. I'm reminded again of that bulb resting underground in winter, "reflecting" on how it will bloom when the season turns, for as Erik astutely phrases it, "reflection cannot help but enable growth." The Two of Swords often implies a choice must be made, and much of the evidence in this reading points to that choice being between serving the self vs. tending to the needs of the collective. The Ten of Pentacles, however, with its harmonious arrangement, suggests some form of cooperation can make both paths possible. I'm noticing that the center of this Ace of Wands image, with its concentration of color and pattern of small dots, echoes the arrangement of "camps" in the Ten of Pentacles.

A healthy city may be the hub that serves its citizens, but each of us can be a hub of energy and resources as well. We can radiate out to engage others with art and ideas, with our personal abundance of whatever kind. We can find the places where our passions intersect with needs of the community. The important thing is that any dormancy be temporary and followed by careful, considered, inspired action – a vibrant unfurling.

Reader: Coleman Stevenson ⓫

Hape Waiu

Poem, Photo & Printmaking: ——————— JORDAN DELAWDER (they/them)

Jordan Kawelo DeLawder (they/them) is a mixed-race poet,
photographer, and printmaker. Their art relates to ecology,
devotional practices, and queer futurity. They live in Portland,
OR and work on a vegetable farm.
@be.holding

I am a calf in a china shop, stumbling onto soft hooves. This is the room that I entered upon birth. Every few feet, there are towers of porcelain like stalagmites, precarious in their reaching. I dare not move or imagine   the catharsis, the shards of sky crashing down.

There is a plate for every memory of every lifetime. People / oceanic / walking about the village / pounding bark for cloth / a woman / women / sitting with other women / beneath the palm tree talking smack / a feral dog / after a rabbit, a cobalt oblivion.

The foremothers are present, shaking their heads with knowing eyes, parting my likeness strand by strand. I am (not) one of them. They show me their secret tattoos: stick and poke hearts on tapioca thighs, rain spells scrawled on ribs,

'Angel (Ancestor)'

great tides of stars lapping at their ankles. They are the ancestors I imagine but   not the ones I deserve. We speak with oyster dribble on chins / faultless / spit and saline. I love them like I love the ocean, like I fear my own body.

I hold the dustpan while Grandma sweeps up the pieces, collecting what's left. She went by three names in her lifetime   but held allegiance to none, discarded

the pineapple rinds behind the retaining wall   and poured buttermilk down the drain   *hape waiu*, she whispers to no one in particular. When my Grandpa died, she shook his mouth and asked her beloved to get up. For the first time   demanded it.

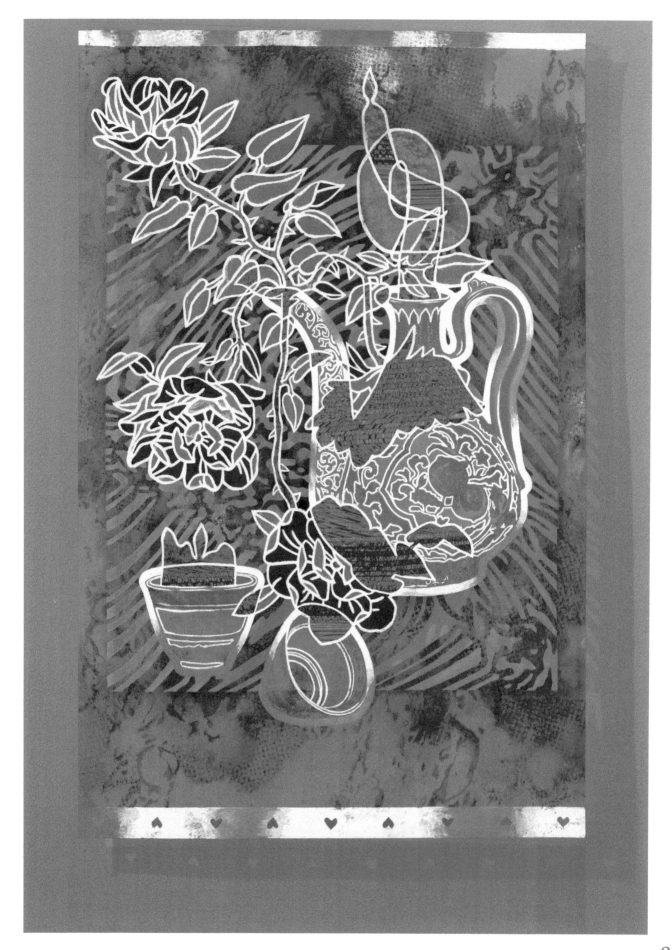

'Full Moon Heart (black light)' by Morgan Rosskopf

'Full Moon Heart' by Morgan Rosskopf

Kill Them with Kindness

Story: STACY BREWSTER *(he/him)*

Stacy Brewster is a Portland-based fiction writer, poet, and screenwriter. He was awarded the 2019 Oregon Literary Arts Fellowship in Drama for his teleplay *Gargoyles & Dandelions*. His fiction and poetry have been featured in *New South, The Gay & Lesbian Review Worldwide, Plenitude Magazine,* and *The Madison Review*. His debut story collection, *What We Pick Up,* was published by Buckman in 2021.
www.stacybrewster.com
@stacybrew

Illustrations: PACE TAYLOR *(they/them)*
Images courtesy of Nationale

Pace Taylor is an artist emotionally preoccupied with Intimacy, and who we choose to share it with. Their work is often quiet, very queer, and persistently vulnerable. They received their BFA in Digital Arts from the University of Oregon (2015), and has shown their work at West Coast galleries including Nationale, La Loma, Oregon Contemporary (formerly Disjecta), and Upfor. Pace is represented by Nationale.
@pacetaylor.jpg

She'd been my teacher, once, Mrs. Mosley. Ruth. At Grover Cleveland High in the late 1970s. English and Latin. I don't remember the grades I got, only that she was fair, if demanding. She kept an office with couches and bean bag chairs that students like me used to hang out in during free periods if only to get in her good graces. We'd recite lines of Ovid or Virgil in Latin as though conjuring spells over a cauldron, and she'd happily join in the dramatics, if not for her own pleasure then to correct our pronunciation, to make us step aside and see how it's done.

Ruth's daughter Rachel was at Cleveland the same time as me, same grade, but in different classes. She is somewhere deep in that sea of children too murky to make out anymore. And when Rachel died, Mrs. Mosley disappeared from Cleveland, and my life, altogether. Until I moved back, until my husband and I found ourselves living right next door to her, not far at all from my old campus. *Her* old campus.

Like so many creatures living in the deep and dark, in the ocean bottom of grief, Ruth Mosley and I have become a kind of hybrid beast over this last year. Not merely neighbors, but freak show twins disappeared by the outside world—linked by fate. But this connection wouldn't last much longer. Ruth was selling, downsizing the way I would have to, eventually. The recent spell binding us together was simply a parlor trick, leftover magic after so many years apart, and it was already losing its potency.

"I woke up under a goddamn tree, Pete!" Ruth said as she entered my garden from hers, finding me on my patio with my coffee and wrestling with one of Kelly's crossword books. Something was wrong. She wore a strange getup and looked haggard, as though she hadn't slept in days.

"What happened to you? What tree?"

"In the park!"

"Kenilworth?"

She looked disoriented as she paused, blinking at me behind cheap painter's goggles, allowing me a moment to take in her outfit: layers of dresses and sweaters, long leather boots with silver buckles, a giant bomber jacket over everything with a matching fur-lined cap that she plopped down on the table beside me. The air around us immediately felt dusty, ancient mink fur swirling invisibly and making my throat tighten. Ruth bunched her long grey hair behind her, knotting it into itself. She looked prepared for a fight.

"Did I miss Halloween?" I said to which there was no reply. "Forgive me, you look like hammered shit," I added, which was always our invitation to each other, a dig to get the blood pumping, to laugh. She gestured toward my house with her eyes and I stood up, held my elbow out for her, and we traipsed the gravel path inside.

"I've had a day," she said, looking about my living room, trying to figure out where to find purchase for the story I knew was coming, perhaps her last story, or the last one I would hear in person before she moved.

I didn't notice it before, but now I could see Ruth was caked in mud on one side of her body, her knit scarves and sweater wet and droopy in places, dry and colorful in others. The rest of her getup made no cohesive sense to me, a hodgepodge, like one of those artist colony games, the exquisite corpse.

"I woke up under one of those big red oaks in the north end of Kenilworth, one with a big knot on the side staring at me, sweating on me, breathing on me like Hamlet's father's ghost come to tell me some detail I'd overlooked. Imagine it, Pete, waking up there among the trees and the overgrown bushes. The furry men in bivouacs, beds they hang between the trees when it's too muddy. You've seen them, with their deconstructed cars and soiled hair, druggy eyes. They stared back at me, not like someone who wanted them to move somewhere, like cops or social services. No, it was worse, Pete. They looked at me with indifference!"

She tore off the painter's goggles, running her fingers through her hair to let it down again, shake some of the cracked mud off it.

"They looked right through me. Like I was a ghost," she added, now beginning to peel off her clothes. "Am I a ghost? Did I die?"

"If you died, you've picked an odd way of haunting me," I said.

"Sorry to strip in front of you, but Monica—god, I can never get over that name!—*Monica* has a final walkthrough with the buyer soon and if she saw a speck of mud on those hardwoods or the staged furniture she has to return, she would shit a poodle. Do you have something I could...?"

I excused myself to grab a stack of spare towels, clothes, and a blanket for her.

We find each other it seems, the widow people, even if we are not so physically close as Ruth and I, our lives spanning twin Victorians, nestled together in the architecture of our neighborhood. But were it different, had we lived a bit further apart, we might very well have found each other across the long summer days of Portland and these empty streets. Because of our history at Cleveland, yes, but also because we'd have glimpsed each other's beacons across the dark, lonely sea of this neighborhood, a neighborhood full of extroverts constantly doing something fun elsewhere, or all packed into one house, one party spilling over into several connected backyards, more popular than Ruth's or mine, a party punctuated with their children's gleeful screams and the music and laughter loud enough to mock the uninvited. Except all that was gone now, the parties at least. The pandemic made sure of that. And now my husband Kelly was gone, too, a lone statistic amid the global millions.

Ruth and I had become our own pod, in the modern parlance, though I hate that word as it reminds me of the first color remake of *Invasion of the Body Snatchers*, with Spock and that dark-haired woman from *Shadows* and Donald Sutherland destined to fail. In our pod, there were times you couldn't tell whose house was whose and which was occupied or abandoned, who picked up the day's mail or let it idle, who read whose paper. No one knew, certainly not me, the one who was twenty years younger than Ruth and, by default I suppose, required to be sharper about such details. Lights remained on, or TVs did, as we swapped locations to find a book we were talking about from the shelves of our twin built-ins, or a piece of art, a magazine clipping, as we got distracted by photographs, stories, our boundless thirst, our petulant bladders. Our two houses slowly became one, where cups and saucers, wine glasses and tumblers, even Trader Joe's snacks earned from long Covid lines of social distancing, leapt freely from one kitchen to the next, so in small and artful ways our lives were ones of magical and constant replenishment.

When I returned to my living room, Ruth was in her bra and a pair of tights over black bloomers. Ruth. Ruth who is selling her house after decades, after everyone in her life has gone and she is finally, perhaps, living her own nightmare, a schoolteacher losing her faculties. Except ever since she'd arrived that morning she looked tanner and more radiant than I'd ever seen her. I flashed on Anne Bancroft as Mrs. Robinson in *The Graduate* and I couldn't unthink it once it was there. As if on cue, Ruth poured bourbon into two tumblers from the bar. *Aren't you going to seduce me, Pete?*

I looked at her as though to say *it's a little early for me sweetheart,* but I took the bourbon anyway.

"Jesus Maude, Pete, quit being such a wuss."

"I have a reputation to uphold."

"I'm sorry, who are you again?"

I cackled and cheers-ed the air between us and she did the same. We both drank.

"Okay, I'm starting to circulate now," she said, wobbling her shoulders then cracking her neck in both directions with the base of her palm.

"Do you need anything?"

"Like a doctor and a straitjacket? Don't patronize me. I see the way you're looking at me. I've not lost it, not yet anyway. I can't get warm and these clothes are destroyed. I'd like to burn the pile out back when we're done if that's okay. Your firepit should do the trick." She stepped back from the pile of her clothes on the hardwood floor, regarding it the way you might a new painting. "Well, I guess the boots won't work. Too toxic. Trash bags," she snapped. "That's best. Get rid of it. Or fire. What do you think?"

I gave her a flannel and a pair of Kelly's sweats. She put on the sweats but not the flannel, choosing instead to dig into the fireplace. "Speaking of fire, why don't we get one started in here." She looked around, unclear where 'here' was.

"No can do. I booked a chimney sweep but they haven't made it out yet."

"No one needs a sweep, Pete. I've never had one. It's soot, black soot, and it's *fine* where it is."

"I see what you did there."

"Such a clever boy."

"I'm serious, though, don't you remember the firetruck last week? I nearly burnt the house down."

"You forgot to open the flue."

"It wasn't the flue. I opened the flue and everything was fine until I lit the starter log, then the room filled with smoke as dry leaves started dropping from the chimney. Squirrels, the chimney folks said. It's common apparently. They're not making a nest or whatever, simply mischief. Can you imagine? Animals hellbent on watching the world burn?"

"You're describing every story on the evening news."

"I suppose you're right. But you really don't remember? The smoke was so bad, I opened my front door. Lonsdales saw and called the fire department."

"You think us old farts have nothing better to do than to stare out our window until something exciting happens. Tell you what, the Lonsdales are nosy pricks. A couple of Kravitzes. You and I both know it was them who called the cops on those Black kids in the park last summer. We talked about it. Don't think I'll ever forget. I'm sure they don't give a shit about you, but what a burned house would do to their property values. When was this, then, your little conflagration?"

"Four days ago, right after I got home."

"I might've heard something."

"You love drama, Ruth."

"True, but I also don't care very much."

She flipped open the flue and leaned her whole torso inside the fireplace as though to give a second opinion.

"Ruth, I'm sorry I haven't checked up on you yet. I've been caught up in my own shit."

She pulled her torso back out of the firebox. "It happened before," she said. "Squirrels, leaves, the fire department. Kelly was too embarrassed to tell you. I don't know why I never mentioned it. The before-times, I guess. Pre-pandemic, before we *bonded*." She said this last word with such disdain, I briefly woke up to myself. What had our relationship been before Kelly died? Polite hellos after we moved in? A discussion about the sagging front fence, or salting her steps during one of the last ice storms? Then months at a time blissfully unaware of who Ruth was, where she came from, or what she was up to.

Ruth bent herself back in to reexamine the flue. "Just because something hasn't happened to you yet, doesn't mean you can't prepare for it," her voice reverberated in the narrow cavity. "Can't they fix your cap or something? Critter-proof it?" Without waiting for an answer, she grabbed the poker and inserted it, along with her entire bare arm, up the chimney, her cheek pressed tight against the air vent, her eyes scanning about the room. I could hear the metal hook of the poker scraping against the shaft as she thrust the rapier up

'Something You Said...'

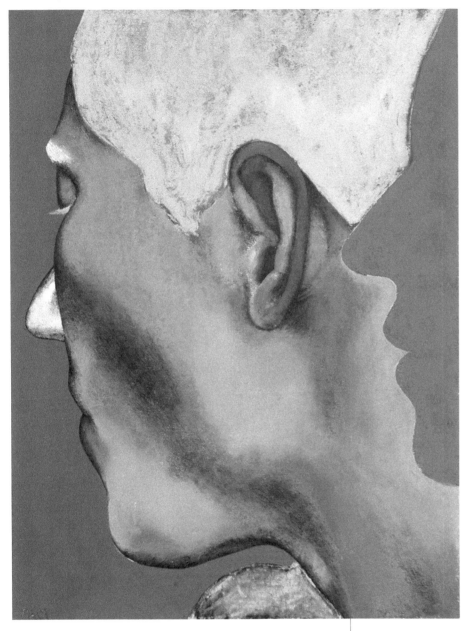

"You know I could have pulled out a space heater, Ruth."

"Thank you, you're very considerate. But fire and bourbon are better."

When the leaves and twigs were ash, Ruth repeated the process until she looked up the chimney flue one last time, her face, her whole body contorted in a squint to report back there was a clean circle of light, no more obstruction. Before I could object, she lit a long match and held it to a starter log, both ends, a trick she'd performed before and tinged with the gleam of the arsonist. She placed it in the fireplace and closed the metal curtain. "Now we're cooking," she said and at last sat on the towels I'd painted the couch with. There were black charcoal smudges up and down the loose skin of the arm she'd stuck up the chimney. And more war paint on her hands and cheeks.

"You ready for this story?"

"Ruth, you could commit hari-kari with the fireplace poker right now and it wouldn't surprise me one bit."

"Pete, I like you because you're honest and because you get so damn fidgety when something's bothering you. Like me! You touch the pulse in your neck with two fingers when you're too nervous to share. You did it when I arrived. But I've got to tell you something. I'm so mad we had to miss our movies the last several weeks while you were on your walkabout thing. Not your fault. I know you're stuck on your book. But darn it, I didn't think I'd miss it so much."

We had turned my TV room into a candlelit den for horror movies. A double-feature every Thursday night. Soda spiked with rum or other booze and loads and loads of buttered popcorn. I don't remember what started it, a conversation about something we enjoyed, jazz maybe, and we decided we needed something outside our comfort zone. A shock to the system. But then I went away for a month. A cabin on the coast to write away from everything. Now it was the week before Halloween, the perfect time for our horror movies, but all I'd sent was a vague, noncommittal text when I got home. In truth, I didn't want to see her because I was embarrassed about how few pages I'd gotten in. I felt like her student again, ignoring the week's assignment.

"I'm sorry," I said. "I saw your car was gone yesterday and

and up with itty-bitty grunts. I imagined Ruth making this same scraping sound on the blackboard to get her students to wake up. The sound drove me crazy and I took too large a gulp of whiskey, wincing immediately at the burn this time. Whiskey was Kelly's jam, not mine.

"Hits the spot, don't she?" she said with a knowing chuckle, her eyes on me now.

As she worked, leaves and twigs fell out and onto the brick hearth, building a pile in the firebox. When she finished, she gathered the branches and leaves up in her arms and walked them out back to the fire pit on my patio, a circle of brick pavers, not more than four feet in diameter. I followed her, picking up what had fallen and then watched as she piled a log, a section or two of last year's *Oregonian*, and lit the whole thing up.

'Afterimage 10'

I worried you'd already moved into your new place. It felt like you were gone gone. Did you get my text? You know you can pop over, use the gate. Why didn't you?"

Ruth grew quiet. She shrugged. Where had she gone?

"Those movies are the things keeping me going these days," she said softly in between long inhales. "Better than one of those treadmill tests they have you do at the cardiologist. The *stress* test. I used my laptop, rented a tall stack of DVDs at the place on Belmont. The clerk walked me through classics and I was impressed by how many we'd seen already! But there were newer ones, foreign ones, recommendations from the kids at the store. Honestly, the gothy squirt spent so much time with me it was weird."

Neither of us had any point of reference with horror. Both of us had avoided the genre our entire lives. Something about the hot tension before the blood, the music telling you what was coming, the intense discomfort. Yet we both took to the experience of watching them together. I cowered behind blankets and fingers, but Ruth never took her eyes off the screen, not for a second. Not for a single drop of blood. She watched it all. And when the credits started, she would slap my knee or squeeze my hand tight and say "Horrible!" But sometimes tears pierced the iron gates of her eyes. "Goddamnit, Pete, I *feel* something. Good for the ol' ticker. I've worked up a damn sweat!"

Each week, she'd go home after our double bill and the following morning she'd come over with coffee and tell me the story of the wild dreams she'd had. Not nightmares—she never had nightmares the way I did, which always surprised me—but wonderful, visionary, bizarre dreams she described the day after our sessions. Horror movie–inspired dreams she'd remember in vivid detail. Like one where she was stuck with Pinhead, the trenchcoated minion from the *Hellraiser* movies with the nails stuck in his face. And the two of them, Ruth and Pinhead, are in this bar full of sailors in Old Town. "Like the one I met Lee in," she'd explained, "except bigger and not so smoky." And here they are, Ruth and Pinhead, and both of them are trying to light a cigarette but they can't because their lighters are out of fluid and it's drizzling inside the bar, this kind of spitting rain. The bartender doesn't have any matches and neither do any of Pinhead's friends, a pack of werewolves. They find this the funniest thing. They laugh and laugh and decide to spend the night with the sailors, playing pool and getting drunk.

There's another one she's told me about. In it, she's taking a shower like in *Psycho*. The dream is black and white and those violins are playing. *Reeh reeh reeh reeh.* But she's not listening to those, she's belting a song to the bath tiles. *And the red, red robin comes bob, bob, bobbin' along, aloooooong.* And when the shadow man on the other side of the curtain comes closer—sexy quiet Anthony Perkins dressed in his mother's clothes—instead of killing her, he starts to harmonize with her so that when it comes time, *she* opens the curtain instead of him and grabs her robe as she steps out. She dances for him and he drops the knife and whistles the tune along with her, pointing his fingers like two pistols, doing a half turn, those wide hips in his mother's house frock, twisting. The two keep singing together as she gets dressed and he *undresses*, removing the wig and frock, the stuffed bra and fraying panties, his hairless chest gleaming in the stark bathroom light, his limp penis hanging there below a light sketch of pubic hair as he jaunts reverently back into the tub to take his own turn in the shower.

"I should have called," I blurted out. "Halloween. The anniversary of Lee's death. I'm sorry."

"Maybe it's best you didn't. And yes, the anniversary. That's what happened, what I've been trying to tell you. I drove to Timberline. I know, why the hell would I go up there? Early-season snow last week, roads should've been hell. But I knew when I woke up yesterday I had to go. My gut told me. Well, all my organs told me. I've been feeling this vibration. All yesterday, but I think it started earlier, a week or longer. And honestly, I didn't know you were home. I didn't see your text. Plus, you have those automatic lights going on and off on timers whenever you're gone. I sort of got a feeling about it like you weren't there."

"What sort of vibration, Ruth?"

"Eyes twitchy, tingly fingers, heart accelerated. A feeling I needed to go back up there and bury Lee. After twenty-one years, it's time. You've seen the box. The sad cardboard number in the hutch. His ashes in a plastic pouch. You're supposed to buy an urn. You're supposed to sprinkle it at sea or some lake where he went fishing, then move on. But it's been there, year after year after year."

It had been ten months for me, but Kelly's ashes were already in the ocean, except for the thimble-full in a locket for his sister in Tampa. No urn. He wasn't here in the house in any physical form, not anymore, except I suppose he was everywhere. In the color I hated in the kitchen, his perfect photos hung perfectly everywhere, the thirty-seven house plants I barely kept alive. The Sondheim musicals on vinyl. And in every scrunched towel on the rack that never dried properly because Kelly was not there to straighten it out again.

"Timberline used to be our happy place," Ruth continued. "Where we got away from it all. Never with Rachel. Just the two of us, on anniversaries and birthdays. We loved it up there. But it was also there on the goddamn mountain where we found out Rachel had—well—you know that story." Ruth blew air through her lips. "I can't scare anyone with the truth anymore. She hung herself in the basement, what more is there to say? It's out there. You know. From centuries ago, you know. Anyway, Lee and I hadn't gone back there since. It's not Mt. Hood to us but Guilty Mountain. And I can see the damn thing from my bedroom window which is the real kicker, ain't it?"

Now that the fire was going strong, she stood with her back to it, gathering the story in her arms, trying to move the energy through wherever it felt stuck in her body. She reminded me of us, her most dramatic and nerdy students, summoning lines of Virgil in her office or belting *Carmina Burana* in the quad.

"So there I was. This box with Lee. This feeling. This vibration. And damnit if I hadn't watched the scariest bloody-mama movie two nights ago, watched the damn thing from beginning to end, people cowered in locked rooms, axe murders, bloody awful, piece-of-shit movie, heart going like a jackrabbit from the opening music to the end credits. And *you* weren't there, damnit. But then I realized. I made it through the night. Not one goofy dream. You know I always have those goofy dreams. It was as though I passed some test. Like that, I snap to it. I'm Captain Nemo off on an adventure."

"Nemo or Ahab?"

"Nemo, I'm not *that* mad! Anyway, I go to Les Schwab on Powell and have them switch me to snow tires. I hit the road right there, don't gas up until Sandy. Stop by the donut shop we loved, had them heat up an apple fritter the size of my face, sugar bright on my fillings as I drive the rest of the way, fixated—no, *obsessed*—with getting up to Government Camp. A fierce vibration now, Pete. If I touch the box of ashes sitting on the passenger seat, I can feel it. And the roads are clear which feels like a sign. I make it up there in an hour and some change. So fast! I'd barely woken up yet and there I was jacking up the emergency break in the parking lot of Timberline, grabbing Lee's ashes, and heading up to the lodge. There's no hole in the top of Mt. Hood like St. Helens. There's no obvious place to put him in, only a million tiny crevices."

"Like my ass these days."

"Pete!"

"But what does that matter, Ruth? When Hood goes, it'll be one giant hole anyway."

"True, but I needed a sherpa, someone to guide me a little ways or take it all the way up there for me. The people summiting start at ass o'clock, though, so it's far too late for any of them."

I flash on Kubrick's adaptation of *The Shining*. Timberline was the model for the hotel Jack Nicholson is hired as caretaker for, the Overlook. The outside at least, for establishing shots. And parts of that exterior rebuilt to scale in a London studio for some of the other scenes. And I remember sitting in my kitchen the next morning after Ruth and I had watched it, not four months ago, grief as raw as a cut onion, crying at everything, and I was waiting for Ruth to show up and tell me a good story when the phone rang, and I'm thinking it's Ruth giving me a heads up she's coming over, but it's not Ruth, it's my editor in San Francisco telling me how much they were disappointed with the latest draft. "You need time to grieve.

We get it. Don't rush," I think their words were. Then the real knives came out. It was too formula, too much like the last one, down to the breed of dog the hero has. It had no spark. Not like the others in the series, they said, somewhere in the middle of a compliment I've already forgotten. Then Ruth popped in through the back gate and I told my editor I had to go and when I told her my story, crying softly from one part to the next, she cheered me up with her dream.

In it, she was Wendy Torrance, the Shelley Duvall character, and she's traipsing around the Overlook late at night and calling to the ghosts there and they start walking with her and telling them their problems and she tells each and every one of them, chanting it with them slow and thoughtful as a poem, *"I release you!"* Then, as she tells it, the chant goes from slow and steady to stern and staccato, from static electricity to quick bursts of lightning shooting bolts from her fingertips. *I release you!* It makes me laugh so hard, I'm crying. And she keeps doing it, shouting now, triumphant, *"IF YOU DO NOT KNOW US AND LOVE US AND HAVE OUR BEST INTEREST AT HEART, GO! LEAVE THIS HOTEL! MOVE TO YOUR HIGHER SELF!! JOIN THE INFINITE, THE SOURCE!!! MOVE ON!!!"* One by one she gets rid of the ghosts of the hotel, including the one possessing her husband who, for some reason, is being played by Paul Newman in her dream instead of Jack Nicholson. "I thought he looked better," she said with a laugh. "Then, after the spirits were exorcised, you could feel spring outside again. The hedge maze looked beautiful, flowers everywhere. As Paul and I go traipsing through it, well, it gets indecent from there, so best to leave it to the imagination."

I release you, is all I keep thinking as Ruth continues her story. I wonder who would try to release us, Kelly and I, once I'd joined him in death, once the new owners here began to assert themselves. New colors, new wallpaper. A new rack in the bathroom. Swapping out all the fixtures in the spirit of restoration, to remind them of the home's first owners, not the last ones.

"I'm in the big Timberline lobby and can't find a guide," Ruth continues. "Someone to help me take the ashes up. If not the top, then somewhere on the trails. I could take a lift but everyone's skiing now and I pictured myself lingering too long at the roundabout, a stupid kid not realizing grandma is up there without skis and I go ass over teakettle into the embankment. I'm also without sunglasses and it's bright as a golden temple everywhere. I must have looked blind roaming the lobby, squinting like this, looking for someone with snowshoes who would know what to do. I could hike up a ways with them, burrow my hands into the base of a tree, an ancient pine resembling Lee—I was sure the tree would speak to me—and then I'd put the ashes there and, season after season, the snow would melt and accumulate, and melt and accumulate again, and Lee would be one with the mountain, its retreating glacier.

"But no one bit at my offer. Everyone avoided me like I had Covid. So what can I do? I bought a pair of sunglasses at the gift shop. I paid for a lift ticket. The boy at the counter didn't flinch. It must happen often, people wanting to go up for a look at the first gate. It does get you high above the lodge with a damn good view. So I sat myself on the moving bench, alone, as another young man fastened the bar down across my lap and then we were going up up up. The sun was brilliant, simply brilliant, and it wasn't cold. It was stunning. A sign, right? And I'm not usually sentimental. So there is part of me enjoying this, but also trying to hold onto the box and to the bar, trying not to look down or behind me, only ahead, to feel it. There are black dots high on the mountain, below the second gate, where you can just make out that the cascading peppercorns are snowboarders and skiers making their runs. And I'm eyeing the landing where I'll be getting off, wondering how far in any direction I can walk to put Lee's ashes somewhere private, where these goofy kids in parkas making stupid jokes to each other, where they at least will not be treading on him, what's left of him. He was, after all, a Navy man and could clock the living daylights out of anyone who so much as looked at him sideways. Even during hospice, I swear he could. His arms were like Popeye's. All he needed was spinach.

"So I'm looking ahead, we're sailing along smoothly, when the whole lift jerks to a stop. I'm not expecting it, and Lee's box of ashes falls from my lap then *whoooooosh* it slides right off the back of the bench before I can grab it. Just like that."

"Ruth!"

"I couldn't see where it landed. I didn't even *hear* it land. Is that not the worst thing I could have done? Then again, I'm waffling here trying to figure out a way to do it and Lee, as impatient as ever, has taken it into his own hands. Tossed *himself* into the mountainside. Can you believe it?"

Ruth puts on the flannel now. She refills her bourbon. She says her back is seizing up and it hurts. She is keyed up. A Lee phrase I'm sure, something he might have said about her when she left the room. Did he enjoy getting a rise out of her? Why is there such an attraction to disturbing the ones we love?

"Well, I got the hell out of there. I'll never find the spot. But he's up there, no denying it. It's not the way I would've wanted, but it must have been the way he did."

Ruth's eyes looked bloodshot now. I got up from my chair and crossed to her, trying to place my hand on her shoulder.

"I don't need that Pete," she bristled, placing her drink on the coffee table then bunching her hair back behind her again, now trying and failing to make a knot. "I don't know what I need, but not that. I'm not one of your characters," she said. I'd been guilty of using bits of Ruth's story in my own work, true, an odd form of immortality to offer someone.

Ruth stared at the fire. I sensed she was nearly done with it, this release. And it would be painful. I wasn't there to participate in what she was going through, but to witness. I wanted Kelly here with me. I didn't want to bear this witnessing alone. Because the future, with Ruth moved away, would mean loneliness creeping in from all sides. Would remind me of those early days before coming out, hiding behind my floppy hair and jean jacket at Cleveland. Or the decade right after, with AIDS hanging over everything and everyone. Losing Terrence first, then Raul, then Queeny Quincy, and Jukebox Jerry. And so many others until it seemed like the war should be over, our numbers thinned out to one maudlin dinner party.

That Kelly and I should survive all that, then this business, the mad king and his acolytes, the pandemic, the squirrel-like mischief makers setting the world on fire? That I should have to survive him now, too, who was always so much healthier? And do it all without Ruth?

It was selfish, but I knew I would begin writing about her again when she was gone. First, because I would miss her company. I'd write about her and her house, a character in its own right, if for no other reason than to alter the course of their destiny. The morning when Ruth was five and her mother's heart seized up, sending her crashing down on the kitchen floor in front of breakfast. The years of fighting with her father to get out of Portland, a feat achieved only after she'd confessed to being whipped by a boyfriend. The boarding school he sent her to. The fire she brought the nasty girls of privilege there. Earning the best grades, a scholarship to Amherst. A college trip to Athens and finding her purpose at last in an ancient civilization, its philosophy, in epic poems she would work at memorizing in their original Latin. Returning to Portland after college to take care of her father's cancer-ridden body. A night out after she'd buried him. Spitting on the feet of a keyed-up sailor at an Old Town bar, a man she'd spend the whole evening sparring with, taming, then eventually marrying. Lee Mosley. Deciding to root down, teach, start a family. Alighting in students like me so many years ago the same passion for Latin and ancient subjects she held so dearly. For the worlds they opened up. For the things they taught us about our own fragile lives, our own false prophets, and plagues.

"A house can trap everything about you inside it," Ruth said, breaking the lingering silence. "The energy doesn't leave when you leave. The house, its bones—what you say about a nice old house, right? How it's got good bones?—they hold onto everything, like our own bodies do. Like the earth beneath us does, building pressure until it boils over. Until there are earthquakes and volcanoes exploding and the rest."

"You know what I do?" I offered. "I light one of those sage sticks wrapped in twine and I go over the windows and doorways and you tell the spirits to move on. 'I release you,' you say, like the dream you told me about, remember? After we watched *The Shining*?"

"I do. But it's not so easy. You know, on the drive home from Timberline yesterday, I felt great. Relieved. I was singing one

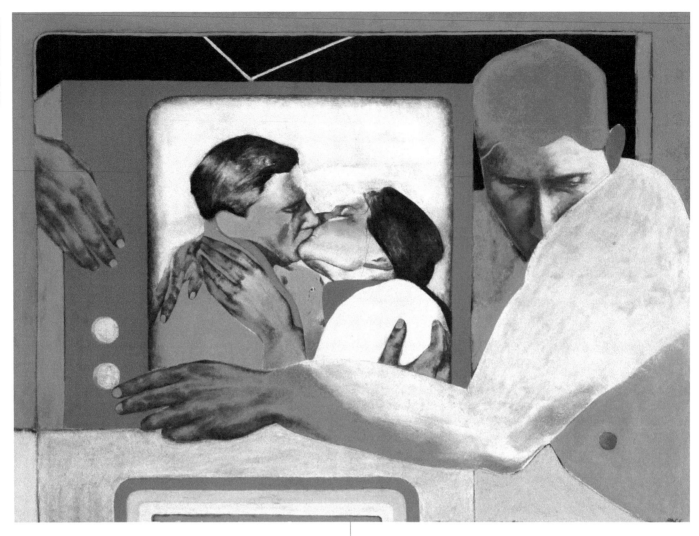

of those Doris Day numbers—*When the red, red robin comes bob, bob, bobbin' along.* I figured I'd get home and put on tea and light a candle or two. I'd wander around the empty rooms and the almost empty rooms, looking at each box I've stacked up for the movers and think: *finally.*"

Ruth grabs my hand. "That feeling went away the moment I stepped back in the house. There was panic jabbing me right here in the chest. You ever have those anxiety dreams where you show up to class without your pants on or the school play is about to start and you've forgotten your lines? Worse, you haven't even *started* to memorize them! Only this was real. I *had* forgotten something. I'd forgotten to go through the boxes under the stairs in the basement. Not many boxes, not much space, but a million memories stored there. My mother's things, letters between her and my father, a couple tins of photos, Rachel's things. My first thought is wanting to burn it, the entire goddamn house, right down to the studs. But I couldn't. You and those stinking Lonsdales might go right up in flames with me, not entirely fair. Or it's like one of our horror movies. Going down alone into a dark basement, which is supposed to mean what exactly? The subconscious? Past trauma? It's very Dante. But I couldn't move. I shivered there, standing in the empty living room, watching the door to the basement loom larger and larger until it was as tall as the ceilings. Stood there like a fool waiting for another sign, waiting for Lee or Rachel, I suppose, to tell me not to be afraid, to tell me everything was going to be okay. *You haven't gotten Covid, lady, so there is grit in you yet. You're still here.* But no one's voice came. No warm embrace, no comfort,

nothing. And it drove me so crazy not to get a signal, a sign, something. So I opened the door to the basement. Nothing came. I turned on the light and stepped down inside, felt the cold clammy wood and the chilly concrete, heard the whir of the gas furnace kick on. Still nothing. I was so frustrated that, one by one, hardly pausing to think what I was doing, I dragged up the boxes from under the basement steps into the living room. Several were too heavy to carry, so I emptied them piecemeal. I lost track of time. My brain sorted as I went. What to trash, what to burn, what I couldn't see a way to part with yet. Do you understand how our lives whittle down to the very dust swirling around us? These records and dishware and photos that must be priceless to you but won't fetch a dime outside your life? Fractions of pennies on the dollar is all we are, I'm sad to report. Don't tell Monica, she's too young to understand. But Pete. Pete! I'm telling you, I sorted through these things hoping to feel something, have my breakthrough. I can feel the energy in these objects but it seems to be traveling right through me. Except every once in a while, there's an object or piece of clothing that seems to vibrate at exactly the same frequency as my body. I hold these objects to me. I put the clothes on thinking I can gather enough energy to feel something. Rachel's fuck-me-boots fit perfectly and two of my mother's dresses, then a third. I stuff them on, one over the next, and Lee's bomber jacket and the scarves my aunt knit me before I left for Amherst, then my father's fur-lined helmet from when he was stationed in Greenland during the war, the remnants of its mink or otter pelt shedding soft pine needles over Monica's pristine floors.

"With these things on, the sound in my head gets louder. There's a machete, too, the one Lee and I used when the neighbor's bamboo got out of hand. I slipped this through my belt. I don't know why, I just did. I liked the weight of it on me. I had everything. A suit of armor like those silly superhero movies. Even a weapon, but no shield. The Greeks and Romans always had a shield, and always helpful for there to be gold leaf or something reflective on it, so you could angle the sun into your enemies' stupid ugly faces. Then I remembered. My father, when he was alive, had a garden out back, but this was before they cut the row of pear trees down, when the back of our house didn't get the afternoon light, not a lick, so he figured out a way to set up mirrors. Not real ones, but panels of tin that, when placed a certain way, reflected enough light onto his starts they did better in summer, thrived actually. Anyway, to stand these pieces of tin up, which were quite light, he had attached a heavy L-bracket on the back, so he could lean them wherever he wanted. And I'd kept them. Rather, I'd kept one, always thinking I'd need it one day for the garden myself. And if I didn't, maybe I'd need a shiny piece of tin to signal to the Lonsdales or you or some kid passing by that I was immobile, stranded by this stupid life. Who knows? But here it was and my arm fit perfectly. My shield and machete in place, my painter's goggles on, and before I knew what was happening, I left the house.

"By now it was the middle of the night, but I had dragons to slaughter, to watch their necks run with crimson. All I could do was wander into Kenilworth Park and begin to do the rounds. If anyone tried to mess with me, I'd rough them up. I'd slay them. If a hot bunny type was taking a midnight walk with their frou-frou shih tzu, I'd kill them both! Slaughter them right there in the park, because what won't we do for our neighborhood, to keep things pure and clean, to keep the gods happy, those vibrating gods needing virgins for their volcanoes! Because you can't kill them with kindness, Pete, that's a myth."

I didn't believe her. There was something in our connection to others, even if you didn't like all the neighbors, you needed them. Even the bad ones somehow.

Out the window of Ruth's and my home is an eighty-six-foot ponderosa pine, so majestic and timeless it takes your breath from blocks away, its light brown trunk straddling the front lawns of our homes, its branches like whole trees themselves, godly muscled arms flexing upward and reaching out in all directions, a tree to make the minds of passersby—our own neighbors with their dogs and looping thoughts—suddenly go blank. The middle-aged hedging, avoiding. The teenagers on their way to school, them too, not a single one wanting to know or see or ever be touched by grief at such an age, despite their righteous protests last year, despite the ever-present pandemic and what it has wrought.

"When I got to Kenilworth, there wasn't a soul," Ruth said. "Not a single creature, not so much as a squirrel lingering long enough for a chat. I grew numb. I didn't feel a thing and forgot why in god's name I was there. My arms and body were so tired from lifting boxes and prying them open, or maybe it was the strain of what was inside them. I found myself so tired I could hardly move, let alone trudge my way home. I meandered, disoriented, light-headed. Had I eaten anything? There was a taste of something in my cheek, some whisky maybe. I fell asleep beside the rhododendrons, under a goddamn tree. And when I woke and saw the machete and everything around me, like the tin shield—no wonder those folks living in the park kept their distance—I left them there and wandered through the park and through the neighborhood until I made it here."

Ruth began to shiver as she sat there clutching her bourbon. The flames still raged in the fireplace, bits of dry wood popping every now and again. I placed an afghan over her shoulders and let her breathe there.

I didn't know how long it would take for her to settle, but it was clear no exorcism was needed anymore. Cancel the priest, Ruth's head has stopped spinning. Because the spirits in her house are gone, every last one. Whether she meant to or not, she'd released them. And in the process, grew young again. She was the sharpest schoolteacher at Cleveland. She accepted no excuses. So many pupils over the years, I bet there's not a day where someone doesn't have an electric charge go off in the folds of their brain in memory of her.

"We've got to figure out what happens next, Pete, what we do next after all this. Another lesson from the Greeks or… No. A horror movie, yes? You with me?"

"I'm right here, Ruth. I'm not going anywhere."

She slapped my knee, hard, then stood up, flinging the afghan off her. "I'll get the stack from my place."

Somewhere a dog was barking. Seagulls cried out. A girl screamed. The world alive, and the two of us still in it.

"Don't sit there, big guy, make us some popcorn." ⓫

Vandoren Wheeler

(he/him), 2022 Recipient of the Buckman Journal Poetry Prize

Vandoren Wheeler was born in Las Cruces, New Mexico with his umbilical cord wrapped around his neck. His luck took a turn when his book *The Accidentalist* won the Dorothy Brunsman Prize, and was published by Bear Star Press. When he teaches, usually in Portland, Oregon, he rarely wears neckties.

93

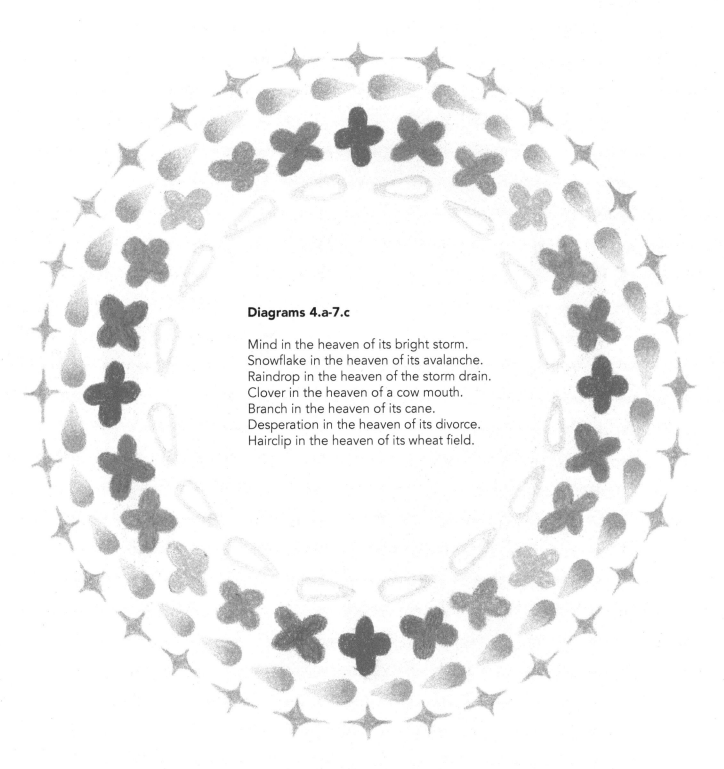

Diagrams 4.a-7.c

Mind in the heaven of its bright storm.
Snowflake in the heaven of its avalanche.
Raindrop in the heaven of the storm drain.
Clover in the heaven of a cow mouth.
Branch in the heaven of its cane.
Desperation in the heaven of its divorce.
Hairclip in the heaven of its wheat field.

Diagrams 8d-9g

Gum in the purgatory of the shoe factory.
Violinist in the hell of arthritis.
Miner in the hell of an MRI chamber.
Seed in the heaven of a sapling,
seed in the heaven of a mouse.
Sapling in the heaven of a campfire.
Rain in the purgatory of a river.
Tree in the purgatory of a bookshelf.
River water in the heaven of the sunlit cottonwood puff balls.

Diagrams 13b-15e

Love song in the jailcell of a jukebox.
Cussword in the jailcell of a crimped mouth.
Fistfight in the doorway of enlightenment.
Lightning across the brainpan of New Mexico.
Water swallow branching the cactus fortress.
The honkey-tonk of teenage cleavage.
Chaw in the juice of a smirk.
Boot swish in the fenced line dance.
Butt sweat in the purgatory of a broken truck.
Tumor in the jailcell of chemotherapy.
Shavings on the workshop floor of prayer.
Wounds asleep in hospital blossoms.
The nerve inside the flinch.
The verve inside the limp.

Diagrams 21c-23a

Crustacean angels hovering the ocean ceiling.
Plastic bag gaping the gorgeous jellyfish.

Butterfly frenching every slutty tulip.
The monotony of the bumble bee orgy.

Seatbelt lint in the bird's nest.
Jackrabbit shackled to laundry grass scent detergent.

Mouse loosed in the heaven of a hawk's claws.
Antlers on the assembly line of the ridge.

Wind washing oaks of crows.
Beetle cleaning this cathedral bear skull.

Diagrams 36b-39d

Art punk in the waiting room of a small town.
Yip in the dark woods auditorium.
Crown feathers clipped in classroom factories,
fur sheared in purgatory detentions.
Obesities uttered from meat factories.
Revolutions after the castrations of focus groups.
Inside jokes inside the jailcells of art galleries.
Protest song in the rest home of a commercial.
Lullaby in the drunk tank of a funeral.

Slender ghost in the waiting room of the deer.

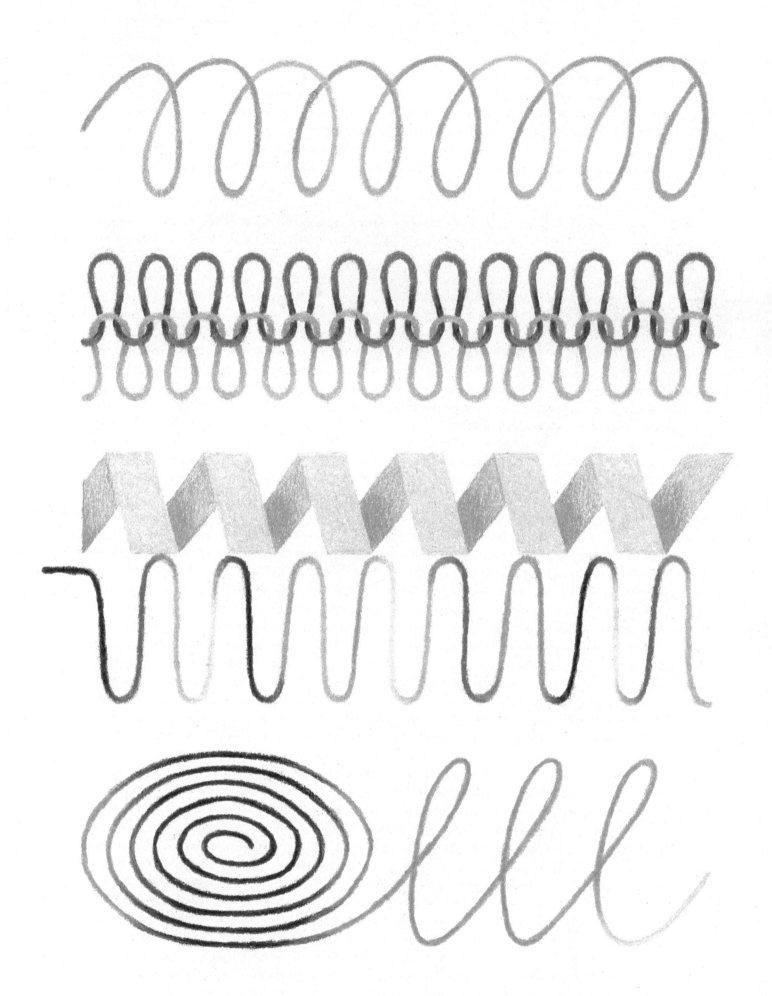

Make/Believe

Here's an old man whittling
a fallen elm branch into
who knows what, maybe
a duck, or a rabbit,
or the smooth knob of
his grandpa's bald head—

the thing he *has* decided is
each cut whispers
its own secret purpose.

    Here's a man knitting his grandmother's
    fingers in a chartreuse octopus beanie.

       Here's some old women
           sewing a song to a sole
              to its shoe.

Here's a girl holding her tongue
       at the exact angle
          needed to thread a needle.

Here we are, making
things all the time.
Not because we always
care to, but to keep our bodies/
brains from turning back
to salt and dust.

Here's a bloody splinter(!)
        that might make
a meaningful bookmark.

       Here's a crow threading
         sticks and ribbon into an empty
      nest his ghost will live in.

        Here's a workhorse dragging
        firewood to burn into fables
        convincing our ancestors
        they'd make it through winter.

       Here's a book sprite(!) spraying
    homemade champagne across
       the mind's electric curtains.

Did you know they slung long
ropes around those boulders,
then wobbled them to Stonehenge
like drunken giants? Can you hear them
shouting the instructions?

        That girl sewing has something
        she's knot saying (!).
        So many bunched stitches to undo.

Here's a spell to turn
    her tongue into a chisel to
          open the collapsed
  cave of her mouth.

Mary Ruefle says you must either
raise your voice above this earthly din,
or whisper to the gods in hopes
the right one hears you.

In some hospital, a brother
wizard flicks his wand to turn
sister into the mermaid
she's dying to become.

        Hey let's make a mini-submarine
        to rescue the teenage soccer team
        trapped in the flooded
        caves of childhoods.

Hey let's tie our shoelaces together—
        okay never mind that's stupid.

Right now two tree
slugs are making out,
making a third slug
twisting its bodies
into slimy spiral taffy.

    Here's a parable in which
our purgatory is to lug around every
      thing we ever bought but
        could have made or borrowed.

Here's a fable in which every
two-eyed creature on earth
looks emotionless into
each human face aghast.

Here's a prayer for the Nigerian prince clacking out
emails just for us, desperate to be heard
above the din of all other princes.

Here's my daughter tying
    hairclips and shoelaces and ribbons
        for no reason, other than
    she's teaching herself to tie long
        thin things together. She loves this

knotty, scraggily mess
because she made it. Plus
it reminds her how yesterday
she couldn't even sketch a decent
box, but today drew a whole
house, then the SUN (!)

There is no need to know exactly
what we're making, except this: that
what you are whittling when
you aren't sure
what you are
whittling is

    a pick for the lock
    The Man will try to chain you
        to the radiator with.

        Swallow it quick.
Practice regurgitating it, nearly
silently, so only
the mice, who will help you, can hear you.

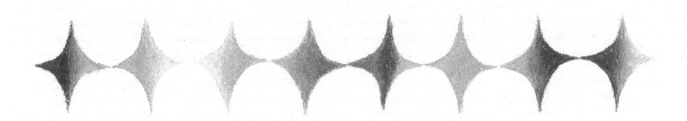

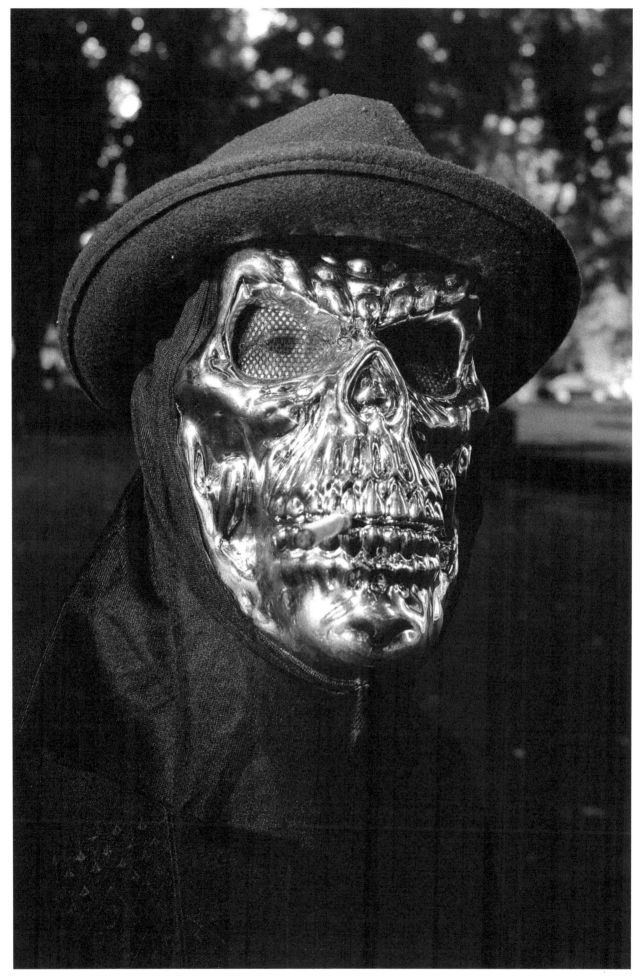

Photos by Chris Nesseth

Corbin's Disposable Camera Snapshots

CORBIN CORBIN (he/him) describes himself as an Intentional Pedestrian. Most of the time he walks around town with disposable cameras and an old hi-8 video camera.
@corbincorbin

Nick Normal plays Lloyd Center

The Lloyd Center claimed to
be the largest mall in the country when it opened
in 1960. It's long been a shell of its former glory, and in the past decade or so
has been passed around between various owners who sway between wanting to revitalize it
or wanting to raze it to the ground. The band Nick Normal figured why not put it to good
use now? They scouted the space beforehand to find somewhere with electrical outlets, and
an entrance nearby for quick setup and getaway. On the day of, we all gathered in the
parking lot — the general sentiment was that if we got thrown out, we'd film that too and
it'd still make a good video. But as the crew ran in and the band began to play, it became
clear that nobody was coming to stop them. We even saw some security guards positioned in
the upper decks, enjoying the show. The crowd of shoppers and mall-walkers that gathered
only seemed disappointed that the band didn't play longer!

Karma Rivera at Rontoms

Karma Rivera at Rontoms for their free weekly Sunday sessions that restarted this summer. Karma is a rapper, and makes some of the best dance music in town. If you're up front you better be dancing because she's not afraid to stop the music and straight up ask you why you're not. I love Portland but we're not a city known for dancing, and Karma has no patience for the "stand and stare" — so I really appreciate her cajoling people into having a good time!

Fabi Reyna at Dig A Pony

Fabi Reyna of Reyna Tropical performing at one of the final nights of Dig a Pony. Dig a Pony was an inner eastside bar known for its crowded dance floor — I think its heyday was behind it, as nobody seemed to express much concern when it closed. I had some good times there! Anyway, the space is now in the hands of the people behind Lose Yr Mind fest, who are reopening it as a music venue called The Lollipop Shoppe, a nod to the early days of Portland DIY (and the legendary Fred Cole of Dead Moon fame). That whole corner of inner SE is becoming a hot spot for live music — while the pandemic led to the end of a few venues, I think even more have opened. Fabi is an absolutely incredible guitar player, she also leads the cumbia-inspired Portland/LA band Sávila and founded *She Shreds* magazine devoted to women guitarists.

DJ Gartex, Strix Varia at Robotripp

That's Bay Area DJ Gartex, and in the second photo she's diggin Strix Varia, known also for guitar and vocals in local band Rhododendron (I also love the person in the background who caught me taking the photo just in time for a pose). This is from the Robotripp rave at a place I'll just call the Factory. I've been to a few events at this space now, but this was my first — I was in awe when I entered, this huge, bizarre space with a beautiful view, occupied entirely by ravers. In the past year, I've been to more parties in abandoned and liminal places than ever before in Portland, and the energy in these spaces is stimulating and contagious. The city may be in a particularly grungy era right now, but some people are putting that to good use.

Rave, Abandoned Research Facility and The Wasteland

The first two are from a fashion show rave at a place known as the Abandoned Research Facility, and the third is from another rave at a place known as the Wasteland. There's definitely an energy at these events that you don't see every day in Portland, and I haven't seen much of in many years. It's coming from the youths — I think when the pandemic hit, a lot of people who were involved in booking and organizing events decided to throw in the towel, which left something of a vacuum. Meanwhile, a cohort of young people were coming of partying age with no ability to even leave the house — so once restrictions started to lift, that energy just exploded into this. I'm definitely something of an interloper in these spaces but I gotta say, the kids are alright — met a lot of kind and wholesome people at these raves.

Fashion Rave

This is from the fashion rave! Same person also came out with a fishing rod and cast it into the crowd. Great impact. And I'll admit, I'm a total sucker for performances that involve fire.

With as many pictures as I have taken, think of all the pictures I haven't. For every photo of an excited crowd, there's countless untaken photos of crowds looking dull, bored, disengaged. While I sometimes might take a picture of such a scene, I typically won't — it's not visually interesting nor flattering, and it just feels like a boring story to tell, even if it may be equally real. My photos are absolutely a documentation of my own subjective reality. ⬤

A NEW FILM BY
THE TRUTH

RACISM
THE MOVIE

C	CURSED ⊛
	ANY PERSON OR PERSONS INVOLVED WITH THIS FILM MUST USE EXTREME CAUTION
RISK MAY INCLUDE MYSTERIOUS CRATES FILLED WITH ABANDONED EPHEMERA AND UNTIMELY DEATH	

Story: CHRIS STUCK (he/him)

Chris Stuck is a freelance writer living in Portland, Oregon. His story collection, *Give My Love to the Savages*, was published in July 2021 by Amistad/HarperCollins. Fiction fellowships include the Fine Arts Work Center in Provincetown, Massachusetts; Callaloo Writers Workshop; and Oregon Literary Arts. He is also a Pushcart Prize winner.

The project had been resurrected yet again, and we were hopeful. But then, during pre-production, right when we were about to get the whole thing up and running, the curse reared its ugly head. Some idiot in craft services decided to come to work with a lethal stomach virus, breathing on every donut, croissant, and everything bagel we had, infecting the entire goddamn crew. It was obvious when the runs and projectile vomiting and the stabbing pains and hallucinations kicked in that luck didn't want to be on our side. And that was just the first day.

When production resumed a month later, we felt so much better that we thought we'd made it through the storm. But then we were just standing around one of the soundstages, smoking cigarettes, when a boom dropped from a great height and hit Dmitry, that Dmitry, the award-winning avant-garde director, the one who'd resurrected the project in the first place, right on his goddamn head.

At his funeral a week later, we all contemplated stopping production then and there. Common sense told us cutting ties with the project and counting our blessings would be a good idea. But just like the previous crews, we thought, like the special little dumbasses we were, that the curse wouldn't get us.

The project had been hanging around the town for decades. No one knew whose idea it was or who originally pitched it. The lore was it had been green lit and then red lit and then green lit for years. And every time a crew ramped up in pre-production, either someone died or a lot of people died or something burned down or an earthquake hit or a Republican was elected president. The project was plain bad luck any way you looked at it, even though it had potential, with Hollywood royalty attached to it here and there. At one time, Eastwood was going to produce and direct, and then Scorsese, and then Coppola. But those might've just been rumors. The project had been passed around so much that most directors considered it sloppy seconds, running from it like it was a Tom Cruise passion project.

In the mid-nineties, some activists got involved, saying they would boycott the project unless the director was Black, which given the project's subject matter seemed like a sound demand. But white studio heads, being white studio heads, claimed they couldn't find any Black directors up to the task, which many of us Black Hollywood grunts thought was a bunch of horseshit.

Until Dmitry, God rest him, resurrected the project, it was perpetually doomed. Even in recent years, when some well-intentioned studio exec would throw a little cash at it, breathe life into it, they'd eventually quit or sexually harass someone and get fired or start doing too much blow and have to go to rehab, and some other well-intentioned exec would change

everything and suck the life right back out of it. Then they'd lose interest, or again someone would die, or a whole crew would die, and the project would go as cold as a grave.

There were seventy-two scripts, so many endless defunct storylines that the whole thing was now just a mess. Eventually, a new white movie, or a comic book movie (often one and the same), would pop up and be a blockbuster. Every studio would look to reproduce that success with something similar, since no one in Hollywood was capable anymore of an original idea. *Racism: The Movie*, though a highly original concept, and maybe too hard to pull off, would then go into limbo again, and everything associated with it, props, scripts, prosthetic noses, would be pitched in a big wooden crate, nailed shut, and thrown in storage like a dead body.

I was the Head PA and having worked on and lived through enough cursed films in my day, I figured I was qualified to call myself the voice of reason. I even thought about calling myself "the sole survivor," but I had respect for the dead, so I thought it was best to just not go there. I once worked on a horror flick where everyone associated with it died in mysterious car accidents. Lucky for me, I hadn't owned a car for the longest and was, therefore, exempt from that curse. On a war film that did a one-week shoot near an old decommissioned nuclear reactor, I was the only one who lucked out and didn't grow extra limbs or start glowing in the dark because I'd gotten the flu that week and called in sick. See what I mean?

Even in my early days, when I worked in the Black adult film industry, those jobs I didn't put on my resume anymore, I was a boom operator for a production that had a freak outbreak of a very rare STD. Again, I was the sole survivor because I was the only one smart enough to go to work in a hazmat suit every single goddamn day. It was the porn industry, after all. It might as well have been Chernobyl. Yet, none of the other production dummies on *Racism: The Movie*, those young white kids, wanted to listen to me. "This could end badly," I kept telling them. "Be ready for it. Don't be surprised when this all goes tits-up."

They said, "Well, if it's gonna be so bad, Marvin, then why are you still here?"

I had a molting stucco shithole out in Toluca Lake and a weirdo son at USC who was on his fourth major, hell-bent on burning up all my money. Like most people in LA, I was so under water on my bills I might as well have been scuba diving. So, what else was I going to do? Go back to waiting tables? I think not.

"Just remember," I always told the youngsters. "In Hollywood, you buy your ticket. You take your chances. And your chances don't mean dick."

A new director was hired, and unbelievably, he was Black, a young kid simply called The Truth, which to me seemed a bit presumptuous since he was only twenty-three. How much truth had he actually encountered in his short life? He'd apparently made a name for himself through his innovative rap videos. Me being old, I didn't expect much out of him, since "innovative" and "rap" didn't often go together in my mind. But, to his credit, he did whip the production into shape quite quickly. He knocked up a script within weeks. The curse, like a fog, seemed to be lifting. People were saying, "See, Marvin? See, old timer?"

I said, "Just you wait. Life has a way of screwing your dog right in the butthole when you least expect it."

Though his name was The Truth, he was pretty short and slight and favored horn-rimmed glasses and berets and for some reason designer kilts. How this total suburban Black nerd made it in rap videos none of us knew. He once explained his vision of the project in his nasally voice. He said, "The film will be a non-linear network narrative that highlights the condition of American life, how we value individuals and not the structure of society, communities. Or do I mean that the other way around?" This was during one of the pep talks he liked to have in the studio parking lot.

He mainlined espressos and yerba mate and speed-talked like a coke junkie, often grinding his teeth. During his little pep rallies, he yelled through one of those old cheerleader megaphones that he always carried around, trying to be nostalgic. He stood on a wobbly director's chair, and we were all thinking the same thing: Watch this poor fool fall and hit his goddamn head. Given how things had gone, we wouldn't have been surprised. I was already thumbing through a list of directors' agents just in case, ranking which of them to call first after this idiot cracked open his walnut.

"The disconnect," he said, "and conflicts portrayed in the film will be displayed through unusual structure and show that racism and bigotry are the result of systemic behavior that overlooks the individual human perspective and makes everything into us versus them, them versus us, mobs, gangs." We all just watched him like students at a lecture, nodding but not really. Evidently, we didn't appear to be as moved by his words as he hoped. There was a long pause, him just looking at us, us blinking at him. "Also," he said, "it'll be about how rich white people just…I don't know…fuck everything up?"

Everyone, even the white folks on set, looked around and said, "Cool, that sounds like it'll work."

There weren't any real hitches for the next couple weeks, which many of us were glad for. We did lose a couple grips in a freak Porta Potty incident, but we were advised by Legal to not discuss it since, you know, pending lawsuits. As far as we were concerned, the incident and all that blood and those obituaries never happened. We forgot about it and set about ramping up, getting the whole goddamn dumb apparatus running.

Things were moving along at a good clip, too, but then The Truth wanted us to excavate all the past production materials. A few other PAs and I went to the old airplane hangar that was the studio storage space. We prepared to crack open the production crate, scared of what we'd find. I approached the dusty thing, sensing something was moving inside. I jammed a crowbar under the lid, leaned on it, and the wood squeaked as the lid opened. Everything seemed fine at first, but then, like a fart out of an elephant's ass, something big and ethereal and ominously orange, flew up and out of there with a screech, flapping its slick wings. It was either a giant flamingo or some otherworldly spirit. Given Racism: The Movie's track record, I was leaning toward the latter.

We took cover and watched the ugly thing do a loop around the rafters of the hangar, gliding, happy to be free but looking like it wanted to bite someone's head off. It was squawking and squealing. It flew out through the open bay doors and into the world with another earsplitting shriek, and we were all standing around, looking at each other with our hands on our hips, like, what the hell was that?

"Well, it was obviously the spawn of Satan," I said, and everyone seemed to agree, me being the voice of reason. "Yep, no doubt about it," we all said. On the way back to the set, we made a pact not to tell the others since none of us had any experience with spawns of Satan and, you know, we already had enough problems as it was.

Thankfully, the spawn didn't seem to have an effect. Maybe it was the albatross that was holding the project down all that time, and now we could thrive. Even I started to think so. The very next day, some big-name actors signed on, Samuel L, Denzel, Morgan. The script had gone through seven rounds of edits and was finalized. Hollywood reporters were starting to talk about the film, as though it was innovative and fresh, a smart blockbuster, that old Hollywood white whale, since blockbusters were usually pretty stupid.

Many of us got a little ahead of ourselves and started talking about Oscars. I wanted to think it, too, but I kept reminding the other grunts that we hadn't even begun real filming. Besides, PAs and grips and gaffers didn't get Oscars. We just got ignored. Also, there were endless goddamn ways this movie, like any movie, could go cockeyed. There were so many films that were once in our exact position but went from the editing room straight to unopened DVDs that were now sitting in the bottom of a landfill.

These young kids didn't know how lucky they had it. I'd risen up the ranks of smaller studios and terribly made films to halfway decent ones. I went from films with nobodies and horrible special effects to true green screens and real actors and real cameras instead of camcorders. Shit, I remembered the '80s and VHS and Betamax, how hard everything used to be, all the chemicals and asbestos and good cocaine we'd been exposed to. I'd been there when that one red emergency phone that was in every production office rang like an alarm bell, with some asshole producer on the other end telling the crew the project we'd sunk our lives into was getting the axe and to go the hell home.

The kids thought I was crazy, that I was being dramatic. They called me MOM, Marvin the Old Man, and CTM, Conspiracy Theory Marvin. But they weren't laughing when one of the sets was found to be haunted. No, those little white kids came screaming my way like I was their family's Black butler. Whenever filming started on this particular set, there was some kind of scream, always when The Truth would yell, "Action!" I thought maybe the spawn of Satan had returned, but it wasn't the screech of a demon condor. To me, it sounded more like a child's scream.

I called a medium to come in and communicate with the spirit quick-fast, and a priest to exorcize it from the studio. It turned out to be the spirit of a young boy who'd died on some film back in the eighties. He'd been mistreated evidently. We asked what film it was and of course he said *Racism: The Movie*, and we all thought, *Crap, the curse is still here*. The whole thing broke us up, though, especially when the kid finally let go of his anger at the Hollywood system and allowed himself to cross over to the other side. "Goodbye, everyone," he said. "I hope your film dreams come true. Mine sure as hell didn't. I got kicked in the head by a fucking horse. But anyway…goodbye."

We all wiped away our tears. "Goodbye, little buddy," everyone said, waving our wet handkerchiefs. "Rest in peace."

As time wore on, the movie started to change, as they all do. Stars dropped out. The biggies, Sam, Denzel, Morgan, were gone. One actor died a quarter the way through, and we had to figure out if it was feasible to CGI him in for the rest of the shoot or just start from scratch. Then more derailments started happening. Inevitably, a studio exec suggested that aliens somehow make an appearance, as well as Black and Mexican gang members, and Middle Eastern terrorists and Russian mobsters, all the Hollywood clichés. The Truth seemed to roll with the meddling, taking the edits in stride, even though it was messing up whatever goddamn mojo we had. He was downing a lot of coffee, slurping yerba like no tomorrow, and the script was growing and growing like some kind of horror movie blob. This was actually quite normal, but a three-thousand-page script was a bit kooky, even by Hollywood standards.

Of course, the film's budget ballooned, too. The movie was just supposed to be about Angelenos, the LAPD, conflicts between Black people and Korean convenience store owners, love and eventual reconciliation across the races, reformed neo-Nazis and KKK members, shit like that. But the studio really believed in it, maybe too much. Now, somehow, we needed to be on location in Bah-goddamn-rain and the Ivory Coast. How far back were we really going to go with the racism? The beginning of time?

We rolled with it, even jaded old me. Just like everyone, I was thinking, *Well, I guess we should be flattered the movie's gotten this far, farther than any other production attempts. Even in spite of the curse, maybe luck and money, a perfect combo in Hollywood terms, was finally on our side.*

But then The Truth started acting funny. I thought he might've been on drugs, but I realized that couldn't have been true. The boy was in his early twenties and didn't look like he'd ever been laid. It turned out, he really was on drugs. But like most youngsters, it was just caffeine, carafes and carafes of whatever he could get. I guess he'd been strung out on the stuff since he was a kid, and unbeknownst to us, he was sneaking it when we weren't looking, shooting it up in between his toes. The coffee shops had really done a number on the boy.

Hopped up on the stuff, he inflated the script again into tens of thousands of pages. We had to halt shooting and pretty much start over, a total revamp. At some point, I printed out the script, and it took up a whole goddamn room. I can't tell you how long it took to do a script read, almost a year. The Truth thought he could make the film about the entire world. He thought he could write every living human's perspective. The yerba had really messed up his brain. "Because isn't that what racism is about, the entire, as you say, goddamn world, Marvin? It's not just America. It's everywhere. It's probably in outer space."

I asked if he was sure he wasn't on drugs.

"No way," he said. "Drugs are evil."

"Said just like someone who's never done them."

I agreed with his sentiment about racism, but at some point, we had to get this thing nailed and start filming again. I told him to save the Bahrain and Ivory Coast stuff for the sequel. Stars we'd signed up to be in the flick were dying of old age. I looked up one day and realized two years had passed since we'd started, and we still hadn't really done a goddamn thing. I had to take the boy's yerba cup and metal straw away from him, switching every cup he picked up with decaf, and then regular herbal tea. I sat up with him as he went through the withdrawals and the sweats. Though he claimed to be one of those weird young kids who didn't do real drugs, I got him a medical marijuana card and some good sticky icky. The dope focused him, made him more artistic, just like I knew it would.

He stopped wearing those dumbass kilts and put on some regular pants. The film finally got back on track.

Of course, just as our mojo got working again, we got word another studio was already copying us, producing a movie simply called *Prejudice: The Film*. It wasn't exactly the same, but it was close enough. Compared to ours, theirs was further along, too, and bore enough of a resemblance to our shit that we suspected we had a mole in our crew. We knew this because we had a mole of our own imbedded in theirs, who was extremely loyal to our cause. I called for a full investigation to weed out the double agent, and it turned out to be Donnie, the newest PA who could never look me in the eyes. We were so far into production, past the point of no return, that maybe we got a little carried away with the punishment. We took him out back of the studio and thought about having him drawn and quartered, which we decided was maybe too brutal, given the crime. Out of frustration, meek little Becky called him a dummy and threw a pebble at him and that seemed to be that. We kept picking up rocks and stones, beaning him in the head until he stopped moving. Everyone on set was sworn to secrecy. We all buried him together so none of us could rat on each other. Then we asphalted over his grave like mobsters and went on with our lives.

Knowing we had to change things up since we were actively being copied, The Truth focused even more and cut the script down from a million pages to a slimmer and more manageable eighty. He went against the dull wisdom of the studio heads and cut out the aliens and other galaxy stuff, all the underwater scenes, the dinosaurs, and focused the whole goddamn thing back to its original kernel: an ensemble cast, a story of interconnectedness, six degrees of racial separation, strife, and redemption.

When I read it, I thought it was utter brilliance, the most intense script I'd ever come across. It was almost an exact replica of reality condensed to ninety minutes. It seemed literary even, if that was possible. The general consensus was we were dealing with a masterpiece, finally, after so long. So, at the end of the day, we didn't feel so bad about stoning poor Donnie to death. He was murdered in the name of art. We revered the script so much that we even handled it carefully like it was printed on ancient papyrus. We all slapped The Truth on the back and said, "Yeah, you did that. You are the truth."

And then, feeling as though I'd saved the day, I told everyone, "See? What did I tell you? Weed. It's the wonder drug."

The whole kit and caboodle went off without a hitch after that. It almost seemed too easy. We were finally doing it.

Those idiots who were copying us decided making their pale knockoff wouldn't be a good look for them anymore, too. They tried to attack a different subject matter, another once-doomed-but-now-resurrected-project simply called *Sexism: The Movie*, for which they'd hired a former rap video director, too, but a woman, a Black woman. Weirdly, we were happy for them. We cheered them on. They'd found their own niche and a way to contribute to society without backbiting and ripping us off. We heard they were having our same problems, too, white studio heads, aliens, a mammoth script, some otherworldly influences, and poltergeists. Though they killed Zack, our mole in their crew, too, we let bygones be bygones and started a weekly softball game and picnic with them. We dug up poor Donnie, and they dug up Zack. We exchanged their battered remains as a sign of unity, which we all seemed to appreciate. Then, again, we went on with our lives, dedicating our respective films to our respective now-dead moles.

It was a long goddamn road, but we achieved what we'd set out to do, where so many other production crews had failed. "A raw, unnerving morality piece on modern problems and urban divide, *Racism: The Movie* examines the menace of bigotry and xenophobia in the lives of interconnected citizens from the City of Angels." That was going to be the movie poster tagline. I have to say that I helped come up with it, me and The Truth on one of our—ahem—"smoke" breaks. The stars had aligned, the movie actors and the actual stars in the sky. It was such a good feeling.

It even turned out that the thing that flew out of the crate, the spawn of Satan, really was just a flamingo that had mysteriously shown up in LA. It had been caught somewhere in Malibu, malnourished. None of us were sure how it survived so long in that crate before we'd opened it years ago. Some vets nursed it back to health and then released it into the wild, where it seemed to be thriving. It had found some other bird to mate with and was now producing offspring, a whole new species, a fact we liked to think was a metaphor for the movie's upcoming and certainly successful release.

That was another thing. The crate. We could finally get rid of it. We were so happy. We'd beaten the odds and the omens and curses. We broke the crate up into pieces and had a little bonfire out in the studio parking lot when editing and the sound mastering was complete. We watched the director's cut and thought, *Goddamn, it really is a masterpiece*. We were feeling ourselves, like we'd conquered the world and racism itself. The Academy, idiots though they were, would really be idiots if they didn't give the film an Oscar, all the Oscars. There was no point in even showing other films that year. Ours was it, the end-all be-all, an eclipse of full totality. We were drinking and carrying on. Some of the crew was making out. Some of us were just having a smoke and maybe a little cocaine.

But then, like a dummy, I turned on a TV and saw the news. The cops killed four Black men overnight in completely separate incidents around LA County. This had been happening for the last few years, cell phone videos, body cam footage, terrible stuff. One had been shot in the back, one choked out, one his neck broken, and one tasered to death. Just the week before, a white cop had "accidentally" shot a Black guy six times in his chest in St. Louis. The same thing in New York and Seattle. There were instant protests in the city now. Fat plumes of smoke rose up all around the valley. People weren't destroying their own neighborhoods for once. They were attacking police stations, mayor's mansions, city hall. It was utter carnage on the screen, like something from a foreign war-torn place, not America. Young Black and Brown freedom fighters were standing up to the National Guard, fighting through tear gas and pepper spray and rubber bullets, throwing rocks and Molotov cocktails at police like it was Beirut or Palestine.

As night fell, the city was throbbing with flames, the blazes throwing flickering shadows onto the mountains like a giant campfire. The Hollywood sign was torched, sparking an inferno in the hills. Protestors were rising up in other cities now, all around the world. The entire globe was smoldering. The oppressed were showing endless solidarity with each other, vowing to eat the rich. And we were standing there with our drinks and joints and coke spoons in hand, watching it, the nonfiction version of our film.

Eventually, while we stood there in shock, one of the red production phones started to ring, and we all knew what that meant. The project was over. It was junk. When The Truth realized it, he cried, bawling like the child he was. Many of the others cried, too, for obvious reasons. Something more important, way truer, and way more absurd than our stupid movie was happening right before our eyes. The world was crap, and we'd just done a movie about it. Who would want to see that?

But me, I wasn't the crying type. Oh, no. I just got some nails and wood and banged up a new crate to put all our crap in, the scripts, the props, the finalized reels. I went over and ripped that red phone off the wall so the goddamn thing would stop ringing. Then I chucked it all in the crate, sinking nail after nail into the lid, sealing it for the next crew of suckers to come along thinking they were saving the world. ⓑ

The Sequence of Summer Dreams

Story: *VIVIAN MCINERNY (she/her)*

Vivian McInerny is a journalist and writer of fiction, essays and poetry. Her children's book, *The Whole Hole Story* was published in 2021 with Versify Houghton Mifflin Harcourt.

Collage: *LARA ROUSE (she/her)*

Lara has been making analog collages since 2017. She uses clippings from new and vintage magazines and books. Her work has appeared in the books *Collage Care* and *Black Collagists*. She enjoys listening to music, traveling, spending time with her family and cutting pictures out of magazines.
@Good_Luck_Lara

She'd left her bedroom window open all night. I slammed it shut. Lucy stirred but didn't wake so I opened the window again, slammed it down a second time, hard. The glass rattled. Lucy rolled over and groaned.

"Mommmmmm!"

"Oh good, you're awake," I said.

My daughter was home for the summer. I say, "Home," but Lucy was out most nights until morning, then slept most days until night. Ok, technically it was just after noon, but the kid was still in bed and I wanted her up.

A couple nights before I woke to the sound of her creeping up the stairs to her room at some ungodly hour and might have fallen right back to sleep if she hadn't stuck her head out her bedroom window and promptly puked. I got up to make sure she was ok, brought her water and a cool cloth, then stared at the ceiling until my alarm went off at six AM and I limped off to work. When I got home that evening, Lucy was having breakfast and clearly had no memory of the night before.

I shook her shoulder.

"What do you want," Lucy whined.

"Time to get up."

"It's Saturday."

"Every day is Saturday to you, but this is my only Saturday this week," I said. "And I want to spend it with the creature I gave womb-and-board to for nine months."

Lucy buried her head under the covers. I'd read all the books when I was pregnant with her. I researched doctors, made a birth plan. I attended every birthing class even though it meant I had to partner with the instructor during breathing exercises because my Dumb Ass Donor, Lucy's D.A.D. and my ex, rarely showed up. When he left us for good, Lucy was barely a year old. I raised her on my own, no other family, nothing. It wasn't easy. All the while, the tiny being that emerged from my body morphed into a million different versions of herself.

Lucy's current incarnation insisted that I respect her "as an independent adult" and blah-blah-blah but here it was past noon and my kid was still curled up in bed with — I'm not kidding— a stuffed SpongeBob SquarePants. Supposedly, ironically, but still. I yanked the comforter from her shoulders, nothing. I raised the bedroom window again and was about to slam it down a third time when she threw back the covers, sat up and cried, "Ok, ok, I'm up. Look! You won. I surrender."

"You're lucky the window didn't break," I said.

A half-hour later, Lucy sat at the kitchen table wearing cut-offs and a ratty T-shirt painting her toenails a bruised shade of blue.

"Get your feet off the table," I said.

"I'm almost done," she said dipping the brush again. I was about to say something when, in an apparent gesture of compromise, Lucy raised her left foot toward the ceiling and made a final swoop of blue in midair. She's very flexible.

Lucy scissored her legs in the air like a synchronized swimmer to dry her toenails. Her toes looked a blur of blue. She used to chew this disgusting turquoise bubblegum in middle school that smelled like a cross between concord grapes and Windex. I tried to recall the *Ten Tips for Parenting Young Adults* article I'd read in a tatty magazine in the dentist's waiting room, but I'd barely skimmed it before the hygienist called me back, and it turned out I needed a crown.

"It looks like an elephant stepped on your feet," I said. "Why would anyone want blue toenails?"

"Because my dress is orange."

"That is a non sequitur. That's like saying, 'I sing off-key because my diary has three-hundred and seven pages.'"

"I know what a non sequitur is, Mom. I go to college." She paused and then added. "How do you know my diary has three-hundred and seven pages?"

"I don't," I said. "The pages aren't numbered."

She laughed. It always felt good to make her laugh. Lucy touched the top of her right toenail to test if it was dry. It was not. She kicked the air some more.

"I had that dream again last night," I said.

"I thought you said you didn't sleep."

"I didn't. Dreams and real life are starting to blur."

Lucy thought I was kidding. I wasn't kidding. Sometimes I felt as if a giant eraser was slowly rubbing out the line that divided sleep from waking life. On a good day, I thought that meant I was about four Ohms short of enlightenment, like I might open my eyes to find myself seated at the feet of Buddha or Allah or Jesus or — who knows? — a pants-wearing sponge. Other times I thought I was going loopy.

"I think I'm going loopy," I said, a little surprised to hear my words aloud.

"It's just a dream, Mom. It doesn't mean anything. It doesn't represent anything. A dream is just your brain trying to process the events of the day."

"So you're a biology major now?"

My daughter had yet to declare a major. My friends told me to enjoy this summer with Lucy because next year she'd probably want to stay back east year-round. That's what their kids did but that's because they paid the rent for them. There was no way I was paying summer rent for Lucy when her childhood bedroom upstairs was empty. I should have said *unoccupied* because her room was anything but empty. It was stuffed chockablock with memorabilia of, what she called, her high school career. Last I checked, a career involved a salary. All Lucy ever earned were good grades and tacky trophies. She did track. She was good, not scholarship good, but good.

She pulled her foot close to her face and blew on her toenails. Yesterday was the first really hot day so she hacked off a pair of perfectly good jeans, expensive jeans. She cut them so short her underwear showed; boy's white Y-fronts. Supposedly, all the college girls wore BVD briefs. It wasn't a gay thing. I asked.

"Do you need to borrow the car or is he picking you up like a proper date?"

"Nice try, Mom. I told you, no date. I'm going out with a bunch of friends. Girls and guys. Emma is picking me up."

"So you're bi?"

"Not everything is about sex, Mom. Do you really not like the blue?"

"It's okay. Where are you going?"

"A little spot on the East side."

"You better not have a fake ID. That is a serious crime, Lucy. I think it's a felony."

"It's All Ages. And FYI, not a felony. More like a wrist slap."

"How would you know?"

"I know."

"So you do have fake ID? Lucy! I swear to God, if you get kicked out of school I'll be so..."

"Rich?"

We both cracked up. Her education was costing me a freaking fortune. She knew that. When she was accepted, her admissions counselor sent a financial aid package that essentially knocked ten percent off tuition, ten freaking percent. For room, board, and coast-to-coast flights, I was on my own. Her father was worthless. Literally, he had no worth, no assets whatsoever unless you count six-pack abs and blond highlights. He surfed. Kurt was essentially middle-aged and never had a real job. But he always had girlfriends, plural. He turned forty-eight last October and his hair was supposedly naturally blond from the California sun. Right.

"Will you please stop talking about Dad's hair? He gets it bleached. Get over it."

I definitely hadn't meant to say those things out loud. Lucy had her dad's hair, only real. It was a rich honey color with golden highlights. My own was a mousey shade of dull.

"In the dream, his hair was iridescent green," I said, "like peacock feathers, only hair."

"Enough with the dreams!"

We'd been talking earlier about my most recent lucid dream. Kurt wasn't actually in it but I didn't want Lucy to know my brain was leaking random thoughts through my mouth.

Lucy stared at the screen of her phone. It lit her skin a pale blue.

"When the giant fish, that was sometimes a rusty Volkswagen, crawled out of the water and licked my hand, I thought: Fish don't have tongues! And suddenly, I became aware of the fact that I was dreaming *while* I was dreaming. I thought, I'm going to make that fish fly, and -voila- he flew! I had total control of the dream," I said. "He rose like a kite, only he was a fish and he wasn't on a string, and he floated across a fiery red sky."

"Fish have tongues."

"What?"

Lucy stopped thumbing her phone long enough to show me a picture of a hideous gray fish, mouth agape.

"Fish FAQ: Most fish do have tongues," she read aloud. "The tongues of fish do not resemble the muscular human tongue. Fish tongues..."

"The point wasn't freaking fish tongues," I said, exasperated.

"What was the point?"

She had me there.

Lucy said she didn't *believe* in lucid dreams as though they were fairies or flying reindeer. For her birthday, I gave her a book written by a respected psychologist who led workshops on lucid dreams. She didn't read it.

"The point is," I said catching the thread again, "when you learn to control your night dreams you gain more control over waking life."

"And you are a shining example of that."

"Are you being snarky?"

"No, I am utterly fascinated by your dreams," Lucy deadpanned, sarcasm dripping like Popsicles in a heat wave.

My very first lucid dream happened when I was about three years old. A tiger chased me through the jungle. It was night. I'd never seen a real tiger but this one looked absolutely authentic with fierce teeth and orange stripes burning bright just like William Blake described, but I knew nothing about Blake back then. I ran, terrified, through the dream jungle. Thick green leaves slapped my face. I felt the sting of them. I felt the tiger's breath hot against the back of my neck. I screamed but no sound came out. Then I had this thought, barely even a thought, more like a mere inkling: *This is a dream.* I turned to face the tiger. And just like that, the big cat stopped. Then, get this, he backtracked! He ran in reverse so ridiculously fast that I woke up laughing at the tiger. Barely out of diapers, and I could control my dreams. You don't have to believe me because it is true.

"Why are you being so snarky," I asked my daughter. "I *am* a shining example of a person in control of her life. People respect me at work. I own a decent car. Maybe my condo isn't up to your

standards, Ms. Hoity Toity College Girl, but I've never missed a payment."

Lucy raised an eyebrow.

"Being late on HOA fees is not the same thing," I said. "I don't know why you are so hard on me and so forgiving of your father's every transgression."

Lucy test-touched her big toenail. Apparently, it passed muster because she finally lowered her feet to the kitchen floor.

"If by 'transgression' you mean 'affairs,' I never felt like those were mine to forgive," Lucy said. "That is between you and Dad."

"Really? You're saying his blatant womanizing has no effect on your life?"

"No, of course, it did, sure. But Dad follows his heart, and I have to respect that."

"His heart! Is that what you kids are calling it these days?"

Lucy grabbed a Coke from the fridge. I used to be able to eat and drink everything and not gain an ounce. It was going to catch up with her one day. Metabolisms shift and slow. She'd see.

"Emma will be here any minute," she said. "I need to get ready."

I never developed a sense of style. I blamed it on the school uniform I was forced to wear during my formative fashion years. Even accessorizing the requisite plaid pleated skirt was a challenge. If I added a cardigan sweater, I looked frumpy. When I wore white knee-highs and saddle shoes, I looked like a Lolita wannabe according to the public school girls. I had no idea who Lolita was, not assigned reading at The Ascension of the Virgin Mary. But I never wore knee-highs again.

Even Sister Josephine accused me of rolling my skirt waistband to hoochie coochie heights my senior year, but really I'd just grown four inches and my mother refused to buy me a new uniform at that point. Once, I was standing at the front of the classroom giving an oral report when the old nun glared at me over her wire-rim glasses. I looked down and realized I was stark naked. The bratty redhead who sat in the front row pointed and laughed. All the other kids just looked embarrassed for me, which was way worse. I was so mortified I said aloud, "This is a dream." And then it was.

But the weird thing was, the girl who sat next to me said, "No, it's not a dream, weirdo." Sister Josephine told us both to be quiet. I had all my clothes on, by the way.

Lucy came back downstairs wearing a bright orange dress with hot pink stripes. She looked like a summer sunset. Her hair, still damp from the shower, was pulled up in a knot on the top of her head which sounds fancy but she was wearing flat sandals and no makeup so the overall effect was effortlessly chic, as fashion magazines writers like to say. I clicked through channels hoping for something worth watching

"Emma just texted," said Lucy. "She's outside."

"Okay." I paused on one of those home shows where someone looks at, buys, and remodels a house in less than an hour. It was a rerun. I hit mute.

"We'll probably be out late. See you in the morning?"

"Probably not," I said.

Lucy raised one perfectly arched eyebrow.

"You won't be up before noon," I said.

"So funny," she said, meaning she didn't think I was the least bit funny.

I clicked the channel changer. Lucy popped the cap off a tube of Chapstick. I found one of those travel shows where the guy flies to exotic places and eats everything in sight and it's always delicious. I kept clicking. Lucy ran Chapstick over her lips several times. She leaned over and kissed me, sweetly, leaving a waxy smear on my

cheek that smelled vaguely of blueberries, and then she was gone.

I landed on a sad documentary about sea turtles. I knew I shouldn't watch TV in the middle of the day but the eggs were hatching and all these tiny, soft-shelled, newborn things started wiggling their way through the sand toward the sea. They were so determined. I closed my eyes and felt myself falling upwards, spiraling without fear through the ceiling and out into a vast night sky. ⓑ

Small Pleasures

Comic: ERIN NATIONS (he/they)

Erin Nations is a cartoonist and illustrator. His comic book series *Gumballs* (published by Top Shelf Productions) won a DiNKy Award and was nominated for an Eisner Award, and an Ignatz. His comics and illustrations have appeared in several publications, and media, including *The Stranger, Eater,* and *Original Plumbing*. He lives in Portland, Oregon.
@elnations
www.erinnations.com

"SMALL PLEASURES"
BY ERIN NATIONS

I COULDN'T SLEEP LAST NIGHT.

I SPENT THE DAY DOOMSCROLLING. I IMAGINED EVERYONE ELSE DOING THE SAME THING, SCARED, ANXIOUS, STRESSED ABOUT THE FUTURE FROM THE AMOUNT OF BAD NEWS OCCURRING GLOBALLY.

WHEN I DID FINALLY FALL ASLEEP, I WOKE UP AT 1:30 AM. I HAD A DREAM ABOUT AN EX. IT WAS THE THIRD ONE THIS WEEK. IN MY DREAM, I LOCKED MYSELF IN A BATHROOM. SHE WAS ON THE OTHER SIDE OF THE DOOR, POUNDING ON IT WITH HER FIST, DEMANDING I OPEN IT. WHEN THE POUNDING STOPPED, I LEFT THE BATHROOM AND WALKED ACROSS THE HALL INTO A BEDROOM. SHE BEGAN TO BERATE ME FOR SOMETHING. I BEGAN TO CRY. SHE SHOUTED, "WHAT'S WRONG WITH YOU?"

IN THE DREAM, I CRIED BACK IN DEFENSE, BUT ALSO ALOUD. MY OWN MUFFLED SHOUTING WOKE ME. I WAS BREATHING HEAVILY.

WHAT DID I DO?!

WHEN THE SUN ROSE, I DECIDED TO GET OUT OF BED AND LEAVE. I NEEDED PEACE. LONG DRIVES, MUSIC, NATURE, COFFEE, AND SUGAR GIVE ME PEACE. THOSE ARE THINGS THAT GIVE ME JOY AND COMFORT.

WHEN I DRIVE, I LISTEN TO THE CLASSICAL MUSIC STATION. THERE'S NO NEWS OR LOUD, OBNOXIOUS DJ. IT'S CALMING WHEN YOU NEED TO CLEAR YOUR MIND OF INTRUSIVE THOUGHTS.

IT'S A CHILLY BUT BEAUTIFUL SUNNY MORNING WITHOUT A CLOUD IN THE SKY. I HOPE YOU'LL STAY TUNED. YOU'RE LISTENING TO ALL CLASSICAL 89.9 KQAC FM PORTLAND.

AFTER DRIVING FOR AN HOUR, I PARKED AT JONSRUD VIEWPOINT. IT'S CONSIDERED ONE OF THE BEST VIEWS OF MT. HOOD IN OREGON. BENEATH THE MOUNTAIN, THE SANDY RIVER FLOWS THROUGH THE VALLEY. THAT MORNING, I HAD IT ALL TO MYSELF.

I WASN'T READY TO GO BACK HOME. EARLIER, WHEN I DROVE TO THE VIEWPOINT, I PASSED A SIGN FOR THE NORTH AMERICAN BIGFOOT CENTER IN BORING, OREGON. I HAD TO CHECK IT OUT! I LOVE AN ODD ROADSIDE ATTRACTION. IT'S SMALL AND MAYBE NOT WORTH $8 ADMISSION, BUT I HAVE NO REGRETS. (I'M STILL NOT A BELIEVER.)

ALSO, I STOPPED IN JOE'S DONUT SHOP. I HAD NEVER BEEN. THE DONUTS WERE OKAY, BUT THEY MADE ME HAPPY.

IT'S IMPOSSIBLE TO ESCAPE THE NEWS. AND I DON'T KNOW IF I'LL EVER GET PAST THE TRAUMA INFLICTED BY SOMEONE IN MY PAST. WHEN IT BECOMES TOO MUCH, I THINK IT'S OKAY TO HAVE A DAY TO ENJOY SIMPLE PLEASURES. SOMETIMES, THE LITTLE THINGS THAT BRING US JOY HELP RELIEVE ANXIETY AND STRESS. I SLEPT BETTER THAT NIGHT.

Oliver Kautter
(he/him)

Oliver is a visual artist based in Brooklyn, New York. He earned a Bachelor's degree in Fine Art with a focus in oil painting in 2014 from Kutztown University of Pennsylvania, then continued his practice in Santa Fe, New Mexico and Portland, Oregon, before moving his home base to New York City. Oliver creates large scale, expressive paintings in oil paint and mixed media. Through observation and social critique, his work provokes an inward reflection and response.

@oak.bklyn

Artist Oliver Agustin Kautter explores the depth of human experience, and not just the nice parts. Much of existence is filled with harsh truths and grim outcomes, and Kautter's time living in Old Town has shaped his art. Amongst the desperate scenes, though, Kautter reveals the resilience, solidarity, and beauty of the Old Town community. Before leaving Portland for the Bed-Stuy neighborhood of Brooklyn, Kautter's final exhibit in Portland, *From the Corner of 6th and Davis*, at Erikson's Gallery was his take on what he saw during the pandemic, the housing crisis, and 2020 protests.

'I Love You'

BUCKMXN: What was *From the Corner of 6th and Davis*?

OLIVER AGUSTIN KAUTTER: *From the Corner of 6th & Davis* alludes to Gil Scott-Heron's debut album, *Small Talk at 125th and Lenox*; a collection of spoken poetry and social critiques, confronting issues that are still relevant today and begging to be addressed. I had already been focusing my work on the true stories of my neighborhood, as seen from my street corner and window on Northwest 6th and Davis. Living through my community's dramatic transformation over the last few years emphasized the significance of capturing this moment in time. I felt especially compelled to share this work and perspective because nobody wanted to set foot in our neighborhood. My home had become a playground for protester's momentary engagement and demonstration, only for them to return home to their utopian neighborhoods on the east side of the Willamette River. In addition to the protests and federal occupation that gained national attention, public mental health crises, open drug use and violence became everyday, broad daylight manifestations. On my bike commute home from work, I had gotten tear-gassed, was barred access to my apartment due to crime scenes, and witnessed three shootings, one of which was directed at me. I loved and took a lot of pride in being a resident of Old Town/Chinatown, and it was difficult to witness the deterioration of my neighbors and our community. My reaction and response were through sixteen paintings and a series of short films that shared these stories.

B: When I look at your *From The Corner* paintings, I think of Miles Davis' album, *On the Corner*, which came out in the same era as the young Scott-Heron. *On The Corner* also captures that inner-city urban living during the tumultuous 1970s.

Tear gas and shootings, these are extreme and horrible things, but I've always believed that artists and writers should be the ones who witness and testify to these events. Who better to document it? How would your art and style change if you played it safer?

OAK: I LOVE *On The Corner*. I actually just listened through that album multiple times while completing my most recent painting. It matched the energy I wanted to capture.

In terms of playing it safer, I think you see the result when you walk through the Pearl District and pass all the galleries. A lot of the art you see is a portal to "the good life", it's conceptual or it's decorative. Sincerely, I never really considered living on the east side (of Portland). I felt in love with and inspired by the life, energy and diversity of downtown. All of the artists who inspire me told stories about their communities indicative of the world at large. This is a formula I've stolen and applied to my work; from Caravaggio depicting everyday people in the storytelling of the catholic church, to Tupac Shakur's debut album *2Pacalypse Now*, telling stories of social unrest and life

as a Young Black Male. The stories worth telling were and still are taking place in Old Town/Chinatown.

B: What made you move to Oregon?

OAK: My parents' history is a major factor in who I am and how I've lived after school. My mother is from Buenos Aires, Argentina, and moved to Queens, New York when she was twenty-one. My father grew up outside of Philly like me, but he moved to Brooklyn after studying architecture in Rhode Island and Rome. When they met in the city and fell in love, they didn't speak the same language. That's the true beauty of New York in particular, but also the beauty of leaving familiarity and going anywhere. I knew from a young age that I was going to seek my own adventure, like you were just saying.

I didn't live up to my potential in high school, which hurt my options for college. Reflecting back on it, I was defiant towards being in Pennsylvania and wanting to be in a city elsewhere. I didn't have close friends in school and was combative with most of my teachers for moving in the opposite direction of what was expected in a public school system. I quit the basketball team because I refused to pray with the team in the locker room before games and was consequently labeled a "cancer." I flunked my final art class not because of the art, but for ignoring the follow-up paperwork. Just about everything felt tumultuous at that period in my life. I had a better experience in college, but four additional years in the same place was more than enough motivation to work harder and move on.

After college, I was offered an unpaid apprentice position for an oil painter in Santa Fe, New Mexico. I had never been to New Mexico, but I saw this as a stepping stone to the west. Within a week of moving, I bought a bicycle, got a job and found an apartment. I wound up only spending one year in Santa Fe, primarily because I was living in an older community in the middle of the desert, and a lot of the art was also landscape painting or geared towards tourism, which didn't speak to my aspirations.

While seeking a better fit for myself and my art, I visited Portland for three days in the summer of 2015 and knew immediately that was my next home. I loved the sense of community and saw a city of young adults who worked and were interested in art, inclusion and the world at large. When I arrived, I didn't have a job or a place to live and I didn't know anyone, but Olympia Provisions hired me as a dishwasher and I eventually found an apartment downtown. I didn't have a lot, slept on the floor and oftentimes worked two jobs to pay rent, but I felt like I had found my home. Over time I learned to cook and advanced within the restaurant, and I eventually moved to a front of house position as a bartender. Bartending changed my life, because it allowed me to afford rent in what became a dream studio AND build a body of oil painting for the first time. My time in Portland developed in me all that I needed to come

'Pink Spring'

to New York.

B: The US is a great country to roam. Not many places in the world where citizens can travel within their country's borders and feel like a foreigner.

So, you had a dream studio, inspiration, what made you leave Portland?

OAK: There were aspects of Portland that I loved and miss, and other parts of it that became too much. Like I mentioned earlier, I witnessed three shootings in the last couple months

I lived downtown, in addition to everything else going on outside (and inside) my apartment. It sounds crazy to say that I moved to New York to be in a safer neighborhood, but it's not. The lack of diversity in the city was also something I struggled with. I have never been labeled "brown" so many times in my life as I was in Portland. I have a hard time identifying who exactly I am or where I "fit in" (my mother immigrated from Argentina, and I was born here but happen to speak Spanish), and to be categorized by others so frequently was confusing and oftentimes came off insensitive. But more than anything, I wasn't receiving enough (or in most cases any) constructive

'Night 93'

art criticism, which is imperative to all artists. To be passively turned away time and time again and left with the assumption my work wasn't safe or decorative enough for the Portland market only meant it was time for a change. To be clear, one co-operative gallery and neighbor in particular rejected this work for three open calls in the last year and a half, including an open call that focused on current events and "lessons we've learned in the pandemic".

I love New York and have dreamed of being here my entire life. It's the city for artists, musicians, actors and dreamers. There's an audience willing to pay for and support your work,

the opportunity to learn from the people from all over the world, and an environment that will push you to get better

B: What are you doing now in NYC? We noticed you walking around SoHo and the subway carrying a large painting on canvas, as if it was a portable art show.

OAK: In terms of my new life, I am starting a new body of work, but I am also focusing on networking and meeting other artists out here. You saw me taking one of my paintings down to Soho for a Rick Owens event at his flagship showroom. The

'Showtime'

concept came from my sister taking me to his store, and me discovering his "grilled-toe" platform boots and watching staff ascend and descend the big stone steps of the showroom wearing such a heavy shoe and large heel—the price of fashion. Listening to interviews, Rick Owens reacted to critics in one interview with the greatest escape: "Either you can relate to it, or you cannot" (the title of the painting). Michèle Lamy, a fashion icon who lives in New York and is married to Rick Owens saw my detail of herself in the painting via Instagram and wound up liking the image and sharing it onto her story. Inspired by this interaction, I carried the painting to the 'A' train and took it to Canal St. and then walked it to the store knowing there was an event that day, and I wound up meeting Paul Soileau (aka Christeene). Christeene is a performance artist and musician who has collaborated with Rick Owens in performance/video art. Exposing my work in person where the scale, expression and color are shared in their true form with successful artists that I admire, felt like a door waiting for me to open on my own. I've been fortunate to have several interactions like this since moving here that I am hoping to use to create new opportunities.

This August I started my first mural commission as well. It is a private mural on a brownstone rooftop, focused on the history of Bedford-Stuyvesant. Our neighborhood is well known because of Biggie, Jay-Z and Spike Lee's *Do the Right Thing*,

but this mural is focused on a somewhat lesser-known history incorporating the likes of Jitu Weusi, Uhuru Sasha Shule and 'the East', meaningful former residents like Ida Wells and Eubie Blake, and the significance of community that makes Bed-Stuy such a unique and special place.

I am balancing these projects and my new body of work with full-time bartending just like I did in Portland. Bartending is still valuable for me beyond paying rent because of the connections that can be forged and applied to my creative practice. I would like to begin shifting focus and work towards making my art the exclusive and financially supportive full-time focus. I often have to remind myself that I'm less than one year into my new life in New York and to be patient, but I'm very excited for my prospects here. ◗

The People of Pithom

Story: J. G. P. MACADAM (he/him)

J.G.P. MacAdam is a disabled combat vet and the first in his family to earn a college degree. His writing has appeared in *Passengers Journal, Military Experience & The Arts*, and upcoming in *Proud To Be: Volume 10*, among others. You can find him hunting for wildflowers with his wife and son.
jgpmacadam.com

Photos: YUYANG ZHANG (he/him)

Yuyang Zhang (b.1993, Wuhan, China) is a multi-disciplinary artist living in Portland, Oregon. Through pop culture references and temporal iconography, his work investigates personal and cultural identities, as well as social and political issues. Zhang's art has featured in exhibits globally, including New Harmony, Indiana; Shenzhen, China; and Berlin, Germany.
@dirtyraccoon

I came downriver following a stream of assurances. *We love you Trying to call you What's happening Don't give up.* But the water was slow and I was too late. The last comment on Schlocky's final post shared only a link to an obituary and the time and place of his wake.

I'm dying inside I wish I was better I love you all

Fucking Schlocky—why'd you do it?

My undercarriage scraped river bottom. Bulrushes tall and slender embraced me. The dockman hollered, "C'mon in! I gotchya. Throw the line!" My rope tapped against the rotted moorings.

The dockman drew me in. "What's your business in Pithom?"

"I come to see Schlocky."

"Schlocky? You mean Stevie?"

"Yeah."

"You knew him?"

"I did."

"And you sailed downriver in that?"

"Sailed? No, more like lucky I didn't end up chum for bottom-feeders."

The roof of my jalopy-turned-bumboat was slick with chop. *Shiphra* was a last-minute slap-together—a hodgepodge hunk of watercraft if one ever was. Her tires spun in the current. A rudder took the place of her muffler. Lashings of log, thatch, pitch and tar were all that kept her afloat. Enough to get me downriver, leastways, and that's all I needed. So I could lay my last on ol' Schlocky.

"You gotta name?" asked the dockman.

"Musa Levi. Yourself?"

"Bobby Reuben." He clasped my forearm and hefted me up.

"Thanks. I'm not too late to see 'im, am I?"

"No, you're not late." Bobby led me down the dock, up the slippery steps, into town. "But you can't see 'im no-how."

"Why not?" The dewy grass soaked my toes all over again; my flip-flops squawking with every step. "I came all this way."

"Well, uh—it's a closed casket, if ya understand."

One glance at the firearm holstered to Bobby's belt told me all I needed to know. One glance at the town of Pithom told me more than I wanted to know.

I knew it, knew all the Pithoms up and down the Ohio, Monongahela, Kanawha, and Susquehanna. My mom and sis raised me in a riverside bungalow, pop skedaddling once the barge business went belly-up, before I skedaddled, too. I left all the Pithoms behind. Nothing but boarded-up Main Streets, plagues of spiraling tax receipts, townships once rich now robbed, feeling cheated, a leeriness and a resentment seeping out of the cracks in their concrete porches, eyeballs scouring you up and down—*now, who's this here?*

"How'd you know Stevie?" said Bobby.

"We were gunners in the same squad—4th squad, Renegades."

"You were in Afghanistan?"

"Yep."

"Oh." Fog hung in the trees, swaddling everything. "Well, thank you for your service."

A great congregation was already gathered within the funeral house. Red roses, white lilies, and blue delphiniums drowned Schlocky's coffin. It was closed. I bade my thanks to Bobby and took a seat in the back, off to the side.

"Jesus sacrificed himself for our sins," said the preacher, "in the same way our servicemen and women sacrifice themselves for our freedom. We owe them no less reverence."

Amen.

A flatscreen scrolled with the sympathies of the townsfolk.

He was a great friend Hard working Fun He was an amazing young man A wonderful father A loving husband Gone too soon Will be truly missed At least he's at peace now May flights of angels guide thee to thy rest.

Fucking Schlocky…

I recognized his fiancé—Zipporah, I believed her name was—from a pic on Facebook, as well as both of their now-fatherless daughters. Their faces dry as salt rock.

They know Schlocky the way I knew him?

Shy guy, on the heavy side. Couldn't run worth a damn. Sergeants always calling him a fat fuck. A fallout. Never once passed his height-and-weight. Though, how fast you ran your two-miler didn't matter one wit when you were deployed. Overseas, you just sat your ass behind a big gun in a turret all day, getting shot at, shooting back. No one ran no two miles in eighty pounds of gear.

A smile splashed onto my face, right there in that pew, remembering ol' Schlocky.

Thinking of this one tic we got in. Schlocky was up in the turret annihilating a packet of chicken teriyaki when an AK-round comes out of nowhere and clips the top of his turret shield. Schlocky drops his teriyaki—bits of it splattering all over me and everyone else down in the cab. He wastes no time racking the bolt of his .50 cal and letting her rip.

"Get some!"

He was a good gunner.

And downright religious over his football. Every Sunday back stateside you'd find Schlocky holed up in his barracks room hollering through a mouthful of nachos at a fifty-two-inch flatscreen. He seemed no different nowadays, by his Facebook pics. A little less hair on his head, maybe, but same pic-perfect smile between cherub cheeks. Same ol' Schlocky. Probably more hair on his back. I would know, from all the times I rubbed tattoo ointment across it. Schlocky got this new tat right after we redeployed. Angel wings down both sides of his back. The gobs of ointment I had to smear on those things—twice daily. Damn, Schlocky, you do this all in one sitting? Yeah, hurt like a bitch. Worth it, though. I'm gonna' fly my ass home with these babies.

Put a frown to my face remembering how he got booted

'Exquisite Gaze'

showing up.

I looked up from my phone. No team of casket bearers requisitioned from the nearest military base stood by waiting to carry Schlocky to his final rest. No bugler, no taps, no folded flag. Not for a dishonorable, and not for a suicide. I looked around at this place, at these people. Told myself it's the same story in every Pithom.

Everett from Muscogee. He made it a whole six months back in the real world before—

Milo from Nantucket, maybe a year.

Jimmy Jameson, from Okeechobee, nearly four.

No one ever posts the real story. About how their husband, brother, son or whatever spent too many hours drinking alone at night. How they bought one gun, maybe two, then chose one of those guns, considered the caliber of the round, the muzzle velocity, tasted it, and then—

No one shares the sticky details. What mother, wife, child or friend or neighbor had the shitty luck of discovering the body, one final trauma to leave as your mark in this world. What 911 medic got stuck cleaning up the mess.

Though, once in a blue moon, maybe, someone posts a note.

I'm dying inside I'm sorry I never expected it to end this way Don't be sad I just need to be with my brothers again I can't take it anymore I feel like I'm losing it No one understands It shoulda been me that died that day Can't deal with the pain anymore I have no choice.

Commiserations follow. A flood of comments, sympathies, likes, hearts, and sad-faces.

Gone but not forgotten Miss u bro Never forget I miss him sooo much May we never forget It was an honor to serve with him A real hero Mama misses you my sweet sweet brave warrior Rest in peace Until Valhalla, brother.

I followed. Someone had to, someone from the ol' platoon. Try to help ol' Schlocky, be there, especially as it became abundantly clear no one else was going to.

The congregation spilled out of the funeral house into the

out.

Schlocky was a shy guy, sure, but put a little liquor in him— or an eightball of coke—and he'd rip the paint off the walls with a karaoke machine. That's what he did, one night, I heard, at a college party off-post. Pissed hot the following week. Our commander told him—considering all the many, many times Private Schlocky fell out of runs—that he had two choices: take the field grade, do your extra duty, stay in the unit, or get out with a dishonorable discharge. Schlocky wasn't dumb. He sensed the way the current was pulling. Our sergeants calling him a fat fuck all the time. Our commander handing him the pen to sign himself out of existence, out of everyone's hair. Schlocky took the dishonorable and a midnight Greyhound home.

Maybe that was why no one else was coming.

A battle buddy needed help—close ranks! I shared and reshared Schlocky's final post. PM'd everyone I could think of. Still, no other Renegades answered the call. The silence was agonizing. So much for brotherhood. I don't know. Maybe everybody else just had too much going on in their post-army lives—budding families, careers, lawns to mow, time zones between most of us. Maybe Schlocky wasn't worth the inconvenience, never was much of a soldier anyhow, not even two years of service under his belt. Maybe I was an idiot for street, many snatching curious glances at me as they flowed past. The townspeople took Schlocky in his box down to the river and they put him on a little reed craft and set a small lit candle in it. Then they sent him on his way down the waters. The people of Pithom stood and watched their son grow smaller, dimmer, until he altogether vanished around the bend. The glimmer of his flame never went out.

"You eaten?" said Bobby.

"No."

"You're welcome to join us."

"Thank you."

The picnic tables sagged with the weight of potato salad, pepper slaw, hog maw, chicken pudding and whatever else could be dished out of a crockpot. Pickled beets, creamed corn casserole, honey cornbread, milk for the children, Pabst and Yuengling for everyone else.

People told stories. They told stories of the Great Flood of '89. "When the water comes, it comes high and fast, you wait and see." "Had to swim outta my trailer in the middle of the night." "No flood wall coulda held it back." "Told those FEMA folks I wasn't evacuating come hell or high water. Well, that high water—it came!"

And people told stories of Stevie.

"He always worked hard."

"Cared about supporting his family, used to drive two hours each way to keep up that job at the Amazon warehouse."

"You remember when we went tubing down the Conodoguinet with 'im? He went to jump in his tube and flipped straight out of it!"

People wrapping big comfy stories around themselves, trying to fend off the damp.

"One day he came and put one of his woodcarvings on my desk. A flag folded into a triangle, you know how they do. Said he wanted to donate it to the police department."

"Boys in green helpin' out the boys in blue, the way it should be."

"Said he was saving up for a pool in his backyard, for his kids."

For dessert they brought out the sweetest smelling apple pie you ever set your nose on. It was still steaming when Zipporah cut into it. The preacher called a prayer and everyone bowed their heads over their slice of pie. "Freedom is not free," said the preacher. "It is paid for in blood. In sacrifice. May we always remember those who have paid the ultimate price."

"Amen."

"To freedom."

"To Stevie."

"Freedom ain't free!"

"Hell, I love freedom!" I slammed my beer down; tapped my cigarette. The preacher clammed up. Heads swiveled.

'Heart of Glass'

"Yes sirree, I love my freedom. Freedom to come and go as I please, freedom to tell my story how I wanna tell it, freedom to own a gun, and use it, to kill you, or you—kill myself, even, if I so choose."

You could've heard a fly cough in that crowd. But it was Schlocky's kids staring straight into me with their big goo goo eyes that brought the shame down upon me.

"I'm sorry…" Clearing my throat. "I'm sorry. Beer's made my lips loose, is all."

Everyone turned their heads back to their plates and stomached their pie, though it was perhaps not as consoling as they had hoped.

That's when Zipporah came and sat beside me. Bobby made to introduce us but Zipporah said, "Oh, I know what you is." She touched my cheekbone. "I can see it. All of us can."

Everyone at the picnic bobbed their heads.

"We need a veteran," someone mumbled.

"What'd he say?"

Zipporah laid her hand on my hand.

"We understand," she said, "how hard it can be to come home." She caressed my knuckles, my palm, her fingertips working magic. "You can come home now, if you want."

The way she kept massaging my hand—made me just want to lay my head on her shoulder and fall asleep.

"Gets cold at night," she said, "in bed, alone."

I yanked my hand back and tried laughing it off. "I think, uh—I may have had a few too many."

Zipporah touched my cheekbone again. "You look like him, you do. Doesn't he look like Stevie?"

Everyone nodded in turn.

"You people must be seeing things, I'm—"

One by one, the townsfolk stood up from their tables and began to swarm around me.

"I'm not sure I under—"

The swarm thickened, closing me in. Everyone wore a piece of Schlocky, I could see that now. Zipporah wore his dog tags. His daughters sporting patrol caps and camouflage tops. An old lady—his mother?—wore his face on a t-shirt. Don't Tread On Me trucker hats. Never Forget online-ordered sweatshirts. Stars n' Stripes bandanas.

"We need a veteran."

"We need a savior."

"A hero."

"A son."

"Hey, now—"

I started to fish my legs out from under the table, but it was too late. People started grabbing at me, wanting to touch me, take a piece of me home for themselves. In my panic and dread, and disappointment, in myself more so than anyone else, I did what I had to do. I reached for Bobby's holstered gun, drew it and pointed it dead-blank in every one of their faces.

"Get back! Back now, ya hear! I *know* how to use this!"

My heart in my eardrums. My feet backing up towards the riverbank all on their own. I'd lost my flip-flops, though one of the good things about not having much is you don't have much to lose.

The people came on like a breaker, threatening to swallow me under with the whites of their eyes. "Why don't you wanna stay?" "We'll take care of you." "Show you the honor you deserve." "A woman will want you." "You're welcome here, Stevie." "Come home, come home."

"Ya can't have me!" I damn near slipped ass-backwards down the dock steps. "Ya can't have me! Stay back!"

They stayed back. And watched me finagle the rope loose and clamber aboard my bumboat and push myself out into the water. I dropped Bobby's gun in the bulrushes.

Plunk.

The current pulled me out into the middle of the flow and the people watched me go.

Downriver a good ways, Pithom long out of sight, night falling and the katydids ringing up a racket, nothing else but the lap of the water and the whistle of wind, the lightning bugs bleeping their butts in the spaces between the blue-lit sycamore boughs, I wondered if I might catch up to ol' Schlocky.

"Not today," I said, lighting a smoke and letting it drift out real slow. "Not today." ⓑ

Death of an Applicant

Poetry: JAYE NASIR (she/her)

Jaye Nasir is a fiction and poetry writer based in Portland, OR. Her work has appeared in *Santa Clara Review, Cellar Door Anthology* and elsewhere.

Paintings: JANICE MINJIN YANG (she/her)

Janice Minjin Yang is a figurative painter and an illustrator. Born in Connecticut, raised in South Korea, Yang explores cultural identities, transformations, and assimilations. She has received a National Scholastic Art Award, and won a 2021 Golden Acrylic Artist Residency in New York. Yang is represented by Blackfish Gallery.
www.janiceyangart.com
@janiceyangart

'Three Faces'

With sudden unearned clarity
I become the morning.
Wake from a dream without faces
with the words on my tongue:
We make rats of our holy women.
Don't ask what it means.
In forming the question you're
already deforming the answer.

Engine revving, beating of wings,
morning is the underside of a dream.
Spring comes early, eats up winter
like a pale green hungry ghost.
I am sure somebody is following me
around in the second dimension.
When I smile at the animals
they think I am baring my teeth.

I cancel all my job interviews
and begin to glow with milky sunlight.
Spit up thistle and extra teeth.
When I try to work I find mold
growing inside the computer,
egg sacs tucked into the circuit board.
Its heat is like a mother's,
its whirring the pulse of labored breath.

Look: it's not the world itself
giving you chest pains,
only the world as advertised.
Any faceless Tuesday can be a sabbath.
Any stranger might be a witch
or a witch's sister, so remember
your pleases, thank-yous and
the cadence of your incantations.

Change itself has a scent,
something dark and wet as birth
in my hair and fingernails.
The best thing to know about yourself
is that you are not yourself.
We make rats of our holy women!
We make rats—!
Carry your disease like a child.

An infestation is only a big party
for the moths. Real saints
have never heard of saints,
as birds have never heard of birds.
Me, I've heard of both.
I'm shedding skin like sleep.
When I bare my teeth at people,
they think I am smiling.

'Fruition' by Janice Minjin Yang

The Rabbit in the Moon

141

Story: SUSAN DEFREITAS (she/her)

An American of Indo-Guyanese descent, Susan DeFreitas is the author of the novel *Hot Season*, which won a Gold IPPY Award, and the editor of *Dispatches from Anarres: Tales in Tribute to Ursula K. Le Guin*, a finalist for the Foreword INDIES. Her work has been featured in *Story,* the *Huffington Post, Oregon Humanities,* and elsewhere. She divides her time between Santa Fe, New Mexico, and Portland, Oregon.

Paintings: ERICA PEEBUS (she/her)

Erica Peebus's acrylic painting dissolves the boundaries between plants and humans with magical realism. Research and documentation are important elements to her creative process. Each painting is an opportunity for Erica to learn and connect to different plants and plant spirits.
@sweet_peebus_art
www.facebook.com/ericapeebus

Legend has it that once every five years, during the first full moon after the fall equinox, all the circus tribes of the West Coast converge on the San Juan Islands. From L.A. come the freaks of Venice Beach, the magicians of the Magic Castle, the DJs and VJs, and acrobats; from Oakland and Berkeley and the City by the Bay come the agitprop street performers and giant puppeteers, the tattooed tango dancers on stilts; from Portland comes the Wonderland Circus, with its feminist burlesque, its elegant aerialists; from Seattle, the Juggling Juggalos and Their Three Rings of Fire. The performers all caravan up the coast in their school buses and tour buses and Sprinters—they've been spotted en masse, on the move—and at the ferry at Anacortes, a fleet of kayaks is involved. There aren't all that many locations in the archipelago suitable for an outdoor festival, but the Circus of the Hunter's Moon, as it's known, never appears in the same place twice.

People claim you can watch, day by day, as the spectacle is assembled—a bevy of Burning Man–style sideshow camps laid out in a long midway before a big-top tent. And when the sun sets on the night of the full moon, the festival begins, with a procession of fire so dazzling sometimes you can see it at sea, and so find your way to it, this secret circus. It's apparently the best party on earth, and it's been going on since the seventies; the islanders are all in on it, but none of them will breathe a word, and of course, there are no posters, no handbills, no directions online. If you want to find it, you just have to go.

Or so Bryce had told them. Bryce being Siler's older brother, who'd lately returned from the summer salmon season in Alaska, looking even more tough and tanned and handsome than he had when he left, Sam thought, if that was even possible. Bryce had sailed up to Anchorage in his own boat, a thirty-footer he'd had since he was sixteen, which Sam couldn't help but find impossibly romantic.

Personally, Sam thought Bryce might have been putting Siler on—at eighteen, she was the youngest in her family, and her siblings were always giving her a hard time, probably because she hadn't sailed around the world yet, or summited Denali, or even set her sights on anything any of them considered ambitious. Ambition was a given with Sam's family as well, but no one expected him to free climb El Capitan or drive a Jeep across the Sahara or backpack through the badlands of Arizona, researching the fairy shrimp of the *tinajas*, the way Siler's brother and sister and parents had, respectively. That's why he'd always felt comfortable among Siler's people; as a bookish, bona fide geek, he couldn't even begin to compete.

That's why Siler was so obsessed with finding this secret circus: no one else in her family had done it.

"Man the tiller," she told him, lifting the binoculars, "and bring her around."

Sam did as he was told, thinking of what his parents would say about that kind of patriarchal language. "To man" was a useful phrase, applicable in any situation where one took responsibility for

a particular post, and much more elegant than "take responsibility for," but of course, implied that women couldn't do the same—"to person" didn't have the same ring. The practice of gendering boats as female, and maybe gendering them in general, was problematic as well. Bryce, no doubt, never considered such things, which was just one more reason it was highly unlikely—impossible, even—that they'd ever wind up together on the deck of his sailboat, entangled in fishing nets and nautical rope, in the course of an adventure of their own...

Siler nudged him with her foot. "Are you even paying attention?" She pointed to the shoreline. "There. Through the trees. What does that look like to you?"

Sam stood up in the wind whipping around the rocky spit and took the binoculars from her. "I don't know," he said, squinting. "A bus? A van?"

"Right," Siler said, "but how did it get there? There's no road. It's just woods around here. This is the wildlife preserve."

Sam shrugged, handing the binoculars back. "Forest Service? DNR?"

But Siler was already tacking hard for starboard.

Sam and Siler were spending the last four days of their fall break sailing the Salish Sea. He'd sailed a bit with her around the Sound, and even as far as Bainbridge, but this was a different proposition, and one that his folks nearly vetoed, until he'd convinced them he'd write an essay about their little adventure, that it would look good on his college applications.

There between the Rosario and the Haro straits, the Strait of Georgia and Juan de Fuca, lay about a million little bony finger islands riddled with keyhole rocks and furred with firs, the smooth red bark of madrones flashing here and there through the evergreens of the temperate rainforest. He and Siler had camped out one night on the beach, and one night in their hammocks, suspended in a coastal tree with arms like landing strips—Sam spotted giant crabs, brightly colored doves, and even the endangered marbled murrelet, which was almost gone now from the mainland, due to the dearth of coastal trees with arms like landing strips—and the night before they'd spent on deck, under a moon the size of dinner plate, under a great wide sweep of stars.

No Physics, no Math Club, no Robotics, no Debate. No college research, college visits, or college essays to write. No discussion of grants and awards, scholarship odds, and tuition calculators—no discussion of strategic majors and minors, growth industries, or the future of work—no discussion of the future at all. Sam and Siler had sat on deck passing a bottle of her mom's Bordeaux between them, and Sam could have sworn he saw, really saw, for the very first time, the rabbit in the moon. It looked like it was running, which struck him as funny; where did it think it was going? Where was it trying to get to—the other side?

As far as Sam was concerned, it would be better if they never found this circus at all. Because maybe if they never found it, they'd never have to go back.

'Bleeding Hearts'

They dropped anchor in a little leeward cove and rowed in on the kayak, slowing for a passing otter. They beached the kayak, wedged it under a boulder above the high-tide line, and climbed the rocky slope to the woods.

It turned out to be a short bus, there among the ferns, covered in faded swirls of colored paint. As they made their way through the forest, branches crunching underfoot, they saw that the windows of the bus were clouded over, the tires were flat, and there appeared to be a tree—an actual tree—growing up through the middle of it. A Doug fir, from the looks of it, right there beside a chimney that had been punched through the bus's ceiling, exhaling a cozy curl of smoke.

Siler stepped up to the door and knocked.

"Greetings!" The voice came not from the bus but from the woods behind them, where an old man with lumpy dreadlocks was stepping lightly through the duff. "What can I do you for?"

Siler lifted her cap, the way she did sometimes, like she was an extra from *The Music Man*. "Hello there!" she said. "Sorry to bother you, but—"

"Oh, no bother at all! You know, I really don't get many—"

"We're looking for the circus?"

The man squinted, his wrinkles rearranging themselves. "Circus?" He shrugged off the pack he was carrying, an old-school canvas number covered in patches and hokey embroidery that might just have been older than he was.

"The Circus of the Hunter's Moon?" Sam asked, feeling ridiculous.

"Never heard of it," the man replied. "But here's a little circus for you!" From his pack, he withdrew five or six little apples just as lumpy as his dreadlocks. As they watched, he began to juggle, with an air of glee that was either alarming or charming—Sam couldn't quite decide which.

The old man's name was Boomer, and he'd lived here in the Turtle Mountain Preserve since 1980, when Mount St. Helens blew. Boomer had been in Portland at the time, at a Grateful Dead Show ("Can you believe it? They played 'Fire on the Mountain'!") and headed north, straight into the ash, which he thought was snow, to see a buddy of his in Seattle, but when he saw the traffic snarled up on the I-5, he kept driving for Anacortes, where he caught the ferry to Orcas. "Wasn't anybody here to say I couldn't," he explained, so he parked the short bus here, at the end of a defunct logging road. As it turned out, all personnel had been dismissed from the preserve to act as support staff for rangers on the mainland, and the preserve's manager turned out to be an old Deadhead himself, so when the staff returned, they were instructed to turn a blind eye to the old hippie in the school bus out there who foraged wild mushrooms and sold them at the farmer's market.

"And since I let Doug there do his thing," Boomer concluded, pointing to the sapling that had grown up through the floorboards, and which he'd cut a hole for in the metal ceiling, "they can't get rid of me without cutting it down, which is illegal on the preserve."

He slapped the table between them, grinning. "How do you like that?"

By then, Sam and Siler were sitting inside the bus over the dregs of their reishi tea, which Boomer insisted upon sharing ("just the thing, this time of year"), and had been for nearly an hour. Which meant it was already noon, and that night was the full moon.

Siler stood, and Sam did too. "Thank you so much for your hospitality," he said.

Siler fit her cap back on her head. "But we've got a circus to find."

Boomer blinked, considering them from within the webwork of his wrinkles. "Absolutely," he said. "You two look like you could use a circus." And then he stood as well. "You know, the person to talk to is Ryan. Hosts a big community potluck—there's one tonight! You should come. In any case, not much, island-wise, gets past him. As for me"—he chuckled—"you might say I'm out of the loop."

Then he stopped, as if someone had spoken, and sniffed the air. "Hmph," he said. "Sea beans soon."

"Ryan?" Siler asked him.

"Stanton. Or Sterling. Bryan Sterling—that's it! Say hello to him for me. And do me a favor, will you?" Boomer leaned in and winked. "Ask him if he's seen the rabbits."

"All right," Siler said. "Will do."

Sam kept his eyes on the forest floor as they made their way in the direction Boomer had pointed them, to the road. (Apparently, there was only one.) There they were, with their packs on their backs, setting out to find this person called Bryan, or Ryan, Stanton, or Sterling, whoever he was, in town. (There was only one of those too.) Maybe at another point in his life, Sam would have wondered what it was he was doing. But at the moment, what he was doing seemed less important than what he wasn't.

"So," he said, finally, "you still thinking gap year?"

Saying the words felt wrong, like he'd broken some tacit agreement between them. But Siler just shrugged. "Yeah," she said. "Haven't told the folks yet, though. Don't know what I'm going to fill it with."

"Backpacking in Patagonia? Climbing K2? Wrestling tigers in the Sundarbans?"

She punched him lightly in the shoulder. "What about you, boy genius?"

Sam shoved his hands deeper into his pockets. "I have decided," he said, "to pursue an apprenticeship in cheese."

Siler didn't laugh, really; she just huffed companionably, like a horse.

"I wish I could take a gap year."

She just furrowed her brow at that. Like, why not?

"You know my folks. They'd freak."

She shrugged. "So they'd freak. So what?"

Easy for Siler to say. She came from a family of iconoclasts, mavericks, extreme adventurers—people who broke the mold. Sam came from a family of doctors, lawyers, and tenured professors—the people who made the mold. They were not gap year sort of folks. They were the sort of people who filled every chink with strategic activities, from early childhood enrichment to continuing education credits, and since he was a kid, every step had been critical: the private schools, the accelerated tracks, the STEAM and the STEM, the science camps and art institutes, the National Honor Society. All of it was supposed to get him into a good college, and then a good grad school, which would give him an edge in an increasingly competitive world.

And yet, despite extensive career counseling, Sam had no idea what he wanted to do with his life. School itself seemed increasingly meaningless, as did anything thereafter. What did any of it matter if the world was slowly being cooked alive? What did it matter if food riots, drought, famine, mass migrations, and cataclysms of every kind were just around the corner?

The future: Not a safe place, as far as Sam could tell.

He looked up, just in time to see a marbled murrelet cruise down the landing strip of a stout coastal tree beside them. It puffed up its feathers and waddled over to a big pile of sticks that appeared to be its nest. The thing looked fragile enough to blow away in the first stiff breeze.

When they reached the road, Sam figured they'd just walk into town—the whole island was, like, ten miles long—but Siler stuck out her thumb.

"What are you doing? We can't hitchhike! There could be a serial killer on the loose."

She gave him a pitying look as a Prius with a little old lady behind the wheel came round the bend. "On Orcas Island? I think we'd have heard."

"Okay, but what about perverts, predators, people of a generally unsavory nature?"

"Good thing I've got you to protect me."

Sam rolled his eyes. If it came down to it, they both knew Siler would be the one to protect *him*. Like both of her siblings, she had a black belt in jujitsu.

"Really?" he said. "Hitchhiking? It's just so..." He trailed off as a truck slowed and then stopped and began to back up. "Seventies."

The truck itself seemed to hail from the same decade, though the driver looked to be in his thirties, a guy with sandy brown hair wearing a canvas vest over a red flannel. "Morning," he said. "Need a lift?"

The guy's name was Wilder, and he'd grown up here on Orcas. After ten years in Seattle as a financial planner ("worst job in the world—you couldn't pay me to take it!") he'd returned from the big city to try his hand at organic farming—or rather, regenerative farming, which was somehow even more organic than organic, in that it sucked carbon directly out of the air and deposited it in the soil.

"Like this," he said—and before they knew it, the guy had both hands off the wheel and was demonstrating this amazing feat of carbon capture with the Altoids tin on his dashboard, which

appeared and then disappeared before their very eyes.

"Whoa!" Sam said. "Could we keep our eyes on the road here? And Wilder, maybe—"

"Not a fan of prestidigitation, I take it?" Grinning, Wilder set the tin back on the dashboard.

"I'd really just prefer..."

The road unfurled as the coast came into view. A kid on a bike watched them from a long gravel driveway, and a young woman, maybe his mother, lifted a hand as they passed. Wilder waved back, and they nearly sideswiped a fence post.

"Jesus!" Siler said, and Wilder laughed.

"All right," he said, "just having a little fun with you. This is my dad's truck, and he's half paralyzed. See?"

Wilder showed them the little joystick thing on the armrest that you could use to steer with your elbow—apparently, his dad had invented it.

Sam cast a glance at Siler as they rolled past one little white clapboard house and then another. "So," he said, after a moment had passed, "where'd you learn to do that?"

"Oh," Wilder said, "it's really nothing once you get over the —"

"No," Siler said, catching his drift, "not the driving, the sleight of hand."

Wilder popped open that tin of Altoids and popped one in his mouth. "You know," he said, "I had a few books when I was a kid."

It was obvious he was lying. Wasn't it? "Have you"—Sam heard himself saying—"ever heard of something called the Circus of the Hunter's Moon?"

"Can't say as I have." Wilder handed Sam the tin. "Care for a mint?"

Of course, Sam popped the lid on that tin, like a dope, and of course, it was empty. Wilder cracked up. "I'm sorry," he said, as they rolled right through a four-way stop, "it's just that everyone else around here already knows all my tricks!"

Sam had figured Wilder would just drop them off in town, but when he heard they were looking for Ryan Sterling, he insisted on taking them directly to the man's house. At that point, they weren't going to refuse.

They found themselves standing beside a driveway, and a little gray-and-black rabbit, half hidden by a Rose of Sharon. Siler crouched down, but the rabbit made no move until she tried to pet it. Then it hopped once, just far enough to stay out of reach, and resumed its nervous nibbling.

"Huh," she said.

"Must be a pet." Sam had been about to say something else, but then he didn't. Because he knew it before he knew it. What was in his back pocket, and how it had gotten there.

"What?" Siler said, seeing his face.

Sam pulled that Altoids tin from his back pocket and presented it to her.

Siler shook her head. "That guy."

"Yeah," Sam said. "Hilarious." He popped open the tin. Inside was a piece of paper, folded over. The note said, *Watch out for rabbits.*

They looked down at the rabbit, then back at each other. Siler shook her head. "What is up with this place?"

The house at the end of the driveway had a porch that sagged, a west-facing window clouded with salt, and one wall in need of siding, but it stood on a hill where you could just see the sea, and it was surrounded by some of the most luxuriant growth Sam had ever seen: mammoth sunflowers leaning on a split-rail fence, dinosaur kale the size of shrubs, and cow tanks bursting with marigolds. They knocked on the door and waited. A sign beside the door said, *Not all who wander are lost.*

Nothing from inside, but they could hear music somewhere out back; there they found a young woman with a pink Mohawk and black hot pants spinning poi in the garden to some sort of bombastic horn music. When she saw them, she let her chains with their bundled wicks spin to a stop and turned down the music on the boom box beside her.

"Howdy!" She lifted a hand, the chain still Velcroed around it.

Though up close, Sam wasn't so certain she was a woman at all, given that Adam's apple and those burly calves. Intellectually, Sam knew there was a whole rainbow of gender expression and presentation, but he really hadn't seen a whole lot of that rainbow for himself. Like most of the kids on Vashon, he didn't have a car, and the only real time he'd spent in the city had been a few field trips for school. "Are you—" he started. "Is your name Ryan?"

"Bryan? No, I'm the caretaker, Gret." And when she spoke, Sam understood that Gret was a transwoman.

"We're looking for a circus," Siler said. "This guy Boomer seems to think Ryan, or Bryan, is the one to talk to."

"Boomer! Love that guy." Gret smiled at Siler, showing teeth. "Yeah, Bry told me we might be expecting you."

Beside him, Sam could feel Siler go still. Expecting them?

"He just got back from the summer season in Alaska. Apparently, he met your brother?" Gret ripped loose the Velcro from her hands and set aside her chains. "As far as the circus goes," she said, with a gleam in her eye, "let me know if you find it. Biggest excitement we've had all year was the big blowdown over Labor Day. What did you say your names were?"

Siler introduced herself, and just as Sam was about to do the same, the bush beside him rustled; that gray-and-black rabbit was now nosing its way along the garden fence, which was all weathered gray wood slats of different heights, with suns and moons cut out of it, like something from the Shire. Sam cleared his throat. "Is that your rabbit?"

Gret laughed, like that was a joke. "Yeah," she said, "that's Harold. And there's Maude, over there"—she pointed down the hill at a white rabbit in a copse of trees—"and that's Matilda"—pointing to yet another rabbit, this one sniffing the perimeter of what appeared to be a hand-built hot tub. Gret looked back at them, amused. "Where did you say you two were from again?"

It wasn't until they returned from this trip that they'd learn the

whole of the San Juans were infested with rabbits, their population originating from a failed breeding operation in the late 1800s. Asking someone if they'd seen the rabbits was basically like asking them if they'd seen the jackalope, only in reverse—they were as common as seagulls in Seattle.

As for where they'd said they were from, they hadn't, so they did.

"Is that right?" And when Gret said it, Sam could hear a slight Southern twang in her voice. "I get down to Seattle now and then. There's a group down there, Hell's Belles, I spin with. Played Pride with them last year." And here Gret must have seen it in Sam's face: Why would anyone so obviously queer live here, on this island in the middle of nowhere, rather than in a big city like Seattle? "But you know," she said, "I like it up here. Came up a few years back, looking for this festival I'd heard about, and sort of just stayed. Haven't paid rent since." She chuckled. "Sort of an artist's residency."

Siler tossed Sam sort of an underhanded glance. "You ever find that festival you were looking for?"

"You know," Gret said, "I never did." Again, that mischievous grin. "You're welcome to wait around for Bryan. Should be back soon."

"Maybe we can help," Siler said. "Getting ready for the potluck, or whatever." The look on her face was as flat as her tone. She wouldn't meet Sam's eye.

Together, they helped Gret stack firewood by the fire pit in the garden (Sam looking away from her handsome biceps as they flexed) and string up garlands of marigolds from the grape arbor (Sam trying not to stare at the girlish grace with which Gret twisted those garlands into place) and harvest potatoes and onions and nasturtiums for the feast ("Go on," Gret said, "try one," and the peppery-sweet taste of the flower exploded on his tongue). Siler reappeared from a wood run with some sort of old-school pop-up tent she'd found in the shed, and Gret laughed. "Good luck with that," she said. "That thing has, like, fifty thousand pieces, and no instructions. Bryan found it at a garage sale."

While Siler wrestled with the tent, Gret showed Sam how to harvest kabochas so the stems would curl as they dried—her deal with caretaking the place was that she got to eat whatever she grew, or sell it at the farmer's market. She also kept chickens, and bees.

"How did you..." Sam was about to ask how Gret had learned all this stuff, but she seemed to read his mind.

"Oh, you know," she said, "I've learned something from just about everybody up here."

Sam cleared his throat. "And spinning poi?"

She smiled. "That's what I teach the people who teach me."

"Maybe," Sam said, almost under his breath, "you could teach me sometime."

"Oh, honey." She laughed lightly. "Give it another few years."

And maybe it was the lush green beauty of the place, the sun

that broke through the cloud cover and gilded the leaves of the grape arbor. Maybe it was the way the garlands of marigolds swayed gently in the breeze. Maybe it was the smell of the sea breeze through that copse of trees, which turned out to be an old apple orchard. Sam found himself following the smell of apples into its midst—found himself lying down on the damp grass there between the trees, his pack behind his head, in the sudden warmth of the day.

He'd had his passing fancies and preoccupations, and had spent the previous summer snogging the bicurious boy he'd met at Space Camp—but until that day, until that very afternoon, the only person Sam had never truly been crushed by, in the truest sense of a crush, was Siler's big brother Bryce. Burly Bryce of the broad hands and shoulders—Bryce, the circumnavigator, mountain climber. Bryce, whom Sam had always known would never in a million years be attracted to a guy like him.

But now girlish Gret, with her slender hands, spinning poi—her whole body swaying in that fine current of tension—Gret, with her bees and kabochas—Gret, digging for potatoes, dirt under her nails, the sharp, dark scent of earth around her—Gret's focused look as she worked...

Gret was a whole new world. A world that might actually have room for him. *Give it another few years.*

Then Sam was out to sea again with Siler, on that clear and windless night, under a moon the size of a dinner plate—it wasn't full yet, and it never would be. Not unless the wind picked up and the boat heaved under the great muscle of it and began to skim along the moon's rippled reflection. Because in this dream they had no motor, and as long as they stayed like that, suspended motionless between sky and sea, time would simply cease to advance. And that was fine, really, because they had nowhere to go, nothing to do—nothing at all they were trying to accomplish. There they sat on deck, Sam and Siler, on the cushions by the boathouse, under the starry sky. Carefully, they passed a bowl back and forth between them—a simple, ceramic thing, made by someone, he knew, who'd dedicated their life to the making of simple, ceramic things—full of something that was supposed to be mead but tasted like nothing at all, its surface reflecting the moon. Sam made his sips as small as possible; as soon as it was done, the wind would start up again, the clouds would race across the sky, and time would move forward.

But no matter how long they sat there, sharing it between them, the bowl never became empty, or even less full...

The cold awoke him, there in the orchard, its gnarled old branches gone black against the twilight blue. As Sam sat up, the grass rippled away from him, and he felt queasy, like some part of him was still at sea.

He stood unsteadily, and again the grass rippled and hitched—and now Sam could see he was surrounded by rabbits. Big ones and small ones, white-gray and dappled, and some as dark as night, their eyes appearing in a flash of fire.

The fire up there on the hill, the bonfire beside the garden. And now that he was standing, he could see it: the fire dancers and freaks, the aerialists and acrobats, the jugglers and Juggalos, the burlesque ladies with their feather boas and boa constrictors, the tango dancers on stilts. The big top tent was big enough for all of this, and more.

Then he blinked, and it was just Gret and a few friends up there spinning poi beside the bonfire, where a small crowd had gathered to watch. To one side was the tent Siler had somehow managed to assemble, and as Sam approached it, climbing up the hill, he saw that a great feast had been laid out on a table inside it: two whole salmon, steamed and laid out on leaves of dinosaur kale, bowls of chips and dips and various baked goods, mounds of mashed potatoes, and many different kinds of cheese, all of it strewn with nasturtiums. Siler was sitting on a folding chair, talking with a man her brother's age with the tanned, rugged look of a sailor; Wilder was doing sleight-of-hand with a handkerchief for a gaggle of giggling kids. The old lady in the Prius was there, and the woman who'd lifted her hand as they'd passed in Wilder's truck as well. Some tweens had taken over the hot tub.

Sam found Boomer smiling at the fire, smoking a little stone pipe. Wordlessly, he passed it to Sam, and Sam took a sniff. It smelled of dirt and Doug firs and campfire.

"What exactly is this?" he asked.

Boomer shrugged. "Just the homegrown. Nothing fancy." ⑬

Photo by Chris Nesseth

More from Buckmxn:

Buckmxn Journal

Buckmxn Journal is a vehicle. An anthology inspired by and made to showcase Portland's literary and artistic talent. Each biannual issue collects the creativity at work in our city and packs full color pages with the work of over 25 local writers and artists across all genres. Open one up and find everything from poems to recipes to essays, photography, painting, sculpture, collage, and beyond. Stories of action, humor and wonder are paired with page-leaping art. Award winning authors and eye-dazzles abound in *Buckmxn*. With a recognition from the Independent Publishers Book Awards, *Buckmxn Journal* is here to keep print media alive and kicking. Issues 001-009 available now.

The Right Tool & Other Poor Choices

Words & Art by Craig Foster

In twenty-three flash fiction stories, Foster presents a succession of bewildered psyches. The quick delivery makes *The Right Tool* the perfect book to crack open when you need an instant dose of someone else's strange. The author also provides illustrations.

Another Fortune & Other Poems

Words by Liz Lampman
Illustrations by Lettie Jane Rennekamp

These boozy poems drip with a queer wisdom, and are anchored by a heroic crown of sonnets. With juicy, emotive watercolors by illustrator Lettie Jane Rennekamp, *Another Fortune* is sure to sweep you up into its sensory reverie and luxurious language.

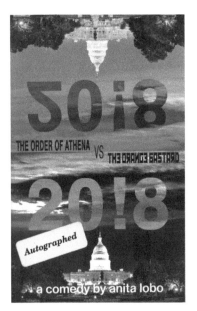

20!8: The Order of Athena vs. The Orange Bastard: A Comedy

By Anita Lobo

Imagine a world in which the title of president gets nowhere near Donald J. Tr***. This version of the world is possible only with the help of a secret order of politically and pant-suit inclined female assassins. *20!8* is an absurdist comedy for anyone who has wondered if we are a living in a glitch in the space-time continuum.

The Last Payphone on the West Coast

By Rich Perin

The Last Payphone on the West Coast is a short story collection of rare realness— centered around folks finding analog moments amongst the age of instantaneous expectation. Told with a tint of the surreal, the twelve stories wander around the North American continent, and are deeply alive with the people that reside in them.

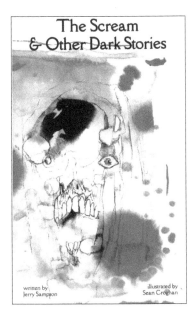

The Scream & Other Dark Stories
Words by Jerry Sampson
Illustrations by Sean Croghan

Deep in the shadows of the human soul are monsters that should never see the light of day. But some fight to the surface, consume the entire being, then prey on anyone else that is around. This is the world of new horror. Artist Sean Croghan provides eerie illustrations.

What We Pick Up
By Stacy Brewster

What We Pick Up is the debut story collection from Portland author and screenwriter Stacy Brewster, recipient of the 2019 Literary Arts Fellowship in Drama. These eleven stories span vastly different decades and landscapes but all manage to mix dark humor, cinematic detail, and sharp prose that turns clichés of boyhood and manhood on their heads.

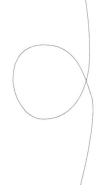

BUCKMXN STORY SERVICE

With the power of the U.S Postal Service, Buckmxn delivers to your door one story a week for ten weeks. It's like a story of the week club featuring the finest writers on the scene, curated by the crew at Buckmxn. Price includes shipping! Wow! Support writers! Support the USPS! $25.00

There are Two Volumes of Ten Stories each to make you & your mailbox happy.

All these titles can be found at buckmanjournal.com
or any reputable bookstore.